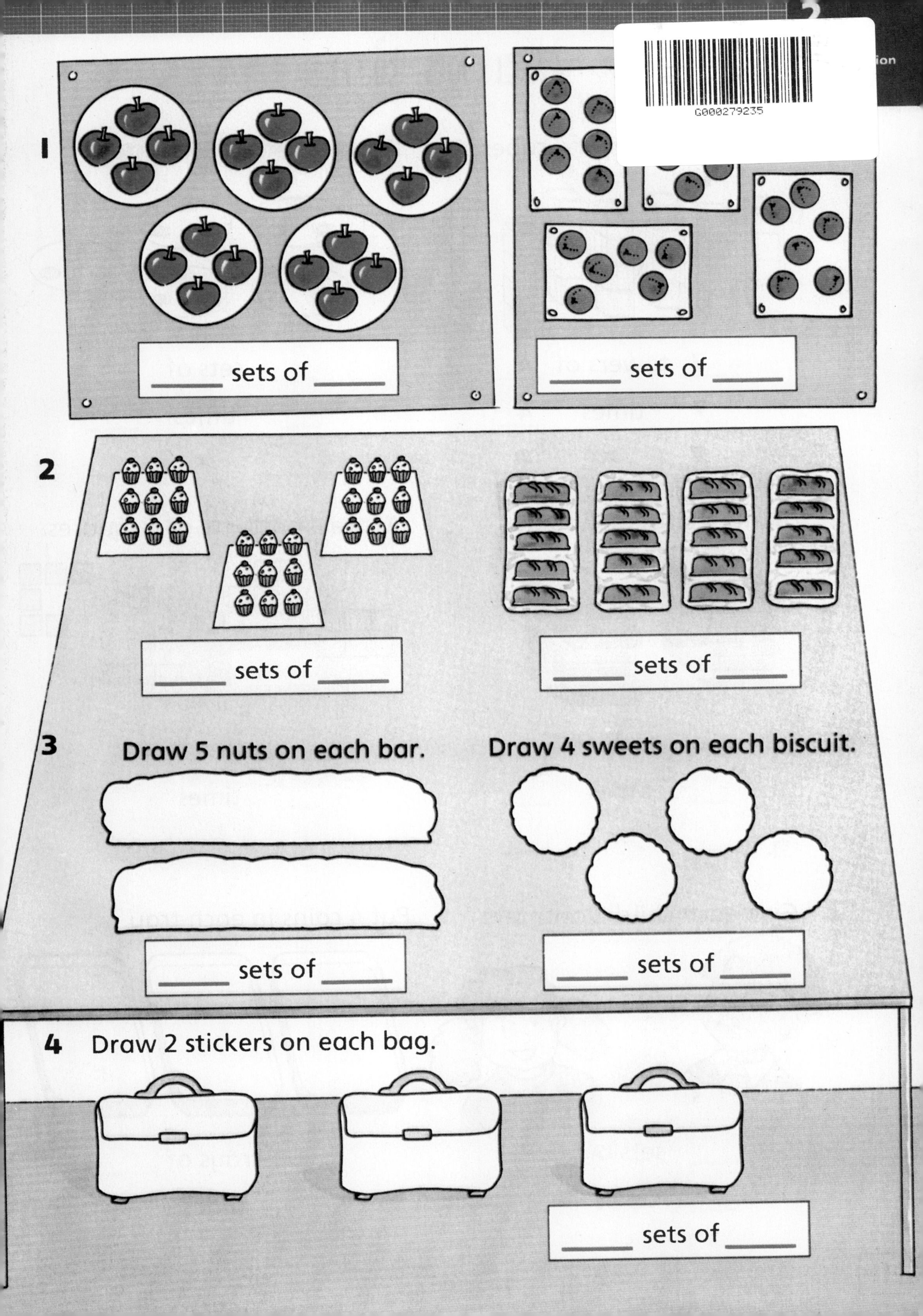

G000279235
1
____ sets of ____
____ sets of ____
2
____ sets of ____
____ sets of ____
3
Draw 5 nuts on each bar.
Draw 4 sweets on each biscuit.
____ sets of ____
____ sets of ____
4 Draw 2 stickers on each bag.
____ sets of ____

Maths time

1 Make 7 towers of 4 cubes.

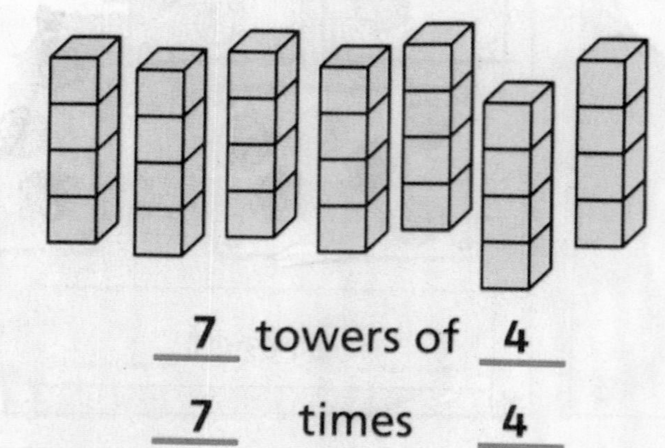

7 towers of 4

7 times 4

7 × 4

Make 5 sets of 3 counters.

___ sets of ___

___ times ___

___ × ___

Build 2 piles of 7 books.

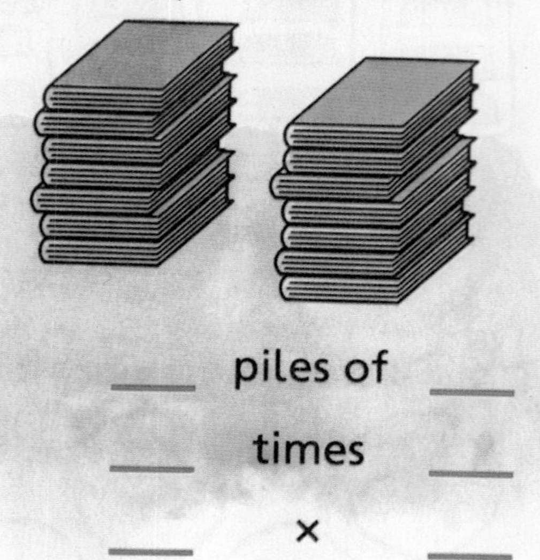

___ piles of ___

___ times ___

___ × ___

Make 4 patterns of 6 squares.

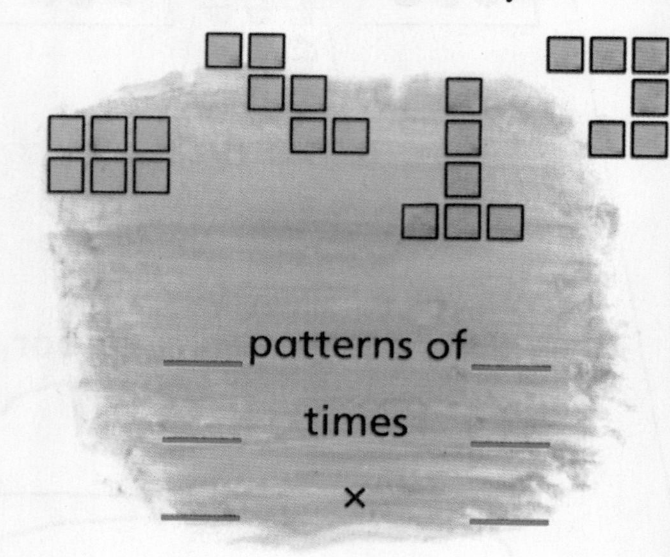

___ patterns of ___

___ times ___

___ × ___

2 Give each child 3 counters.

___ sets of ___

___ times ___

___ × ___

Put 4 coins in each tray.

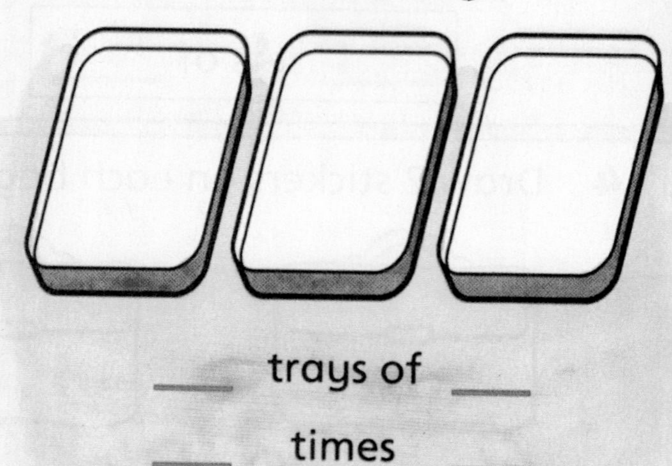

___ trays of ___

___ times ___

___ × ___

Computer games

1

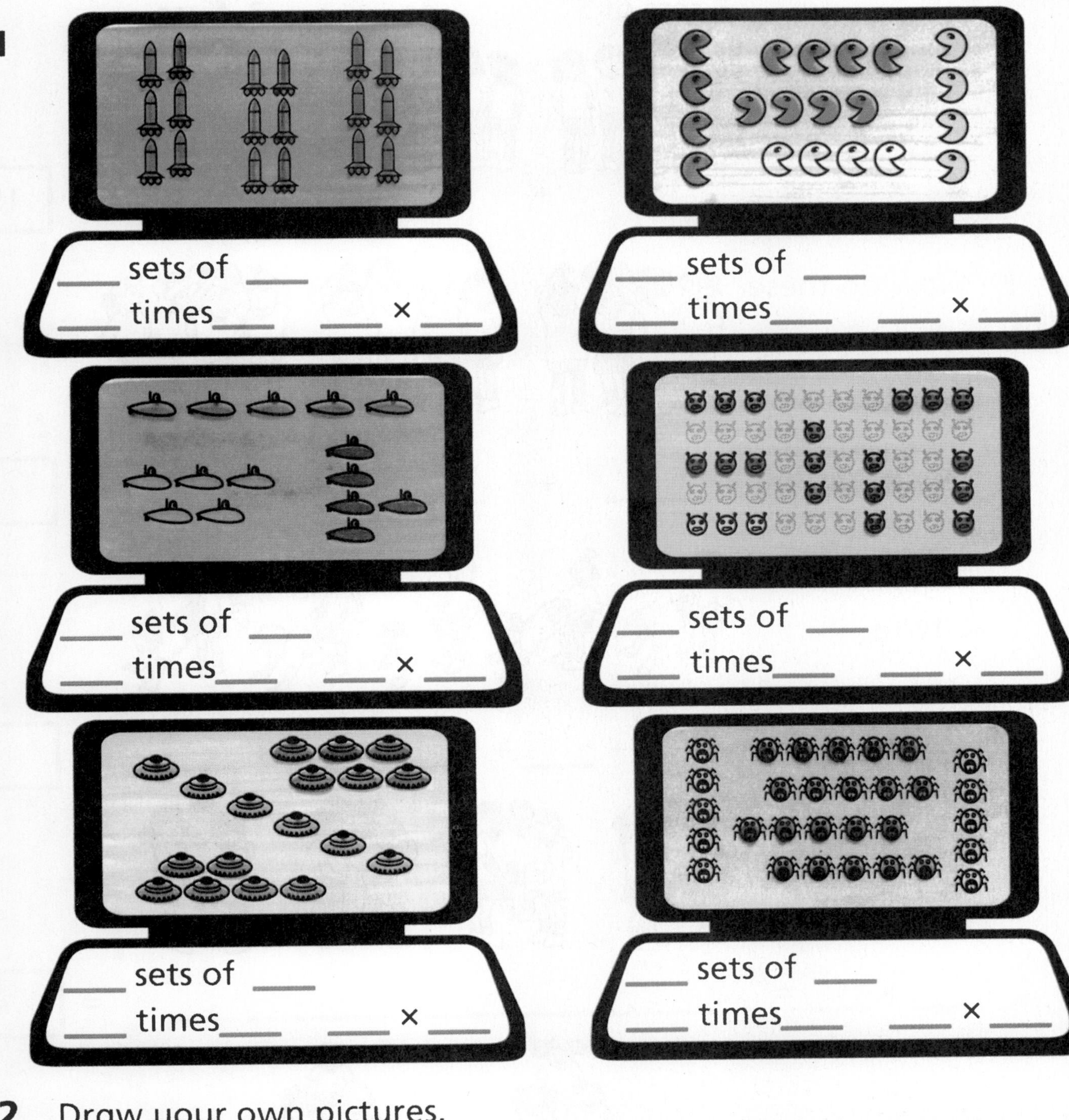

2 Draw your own pictures.

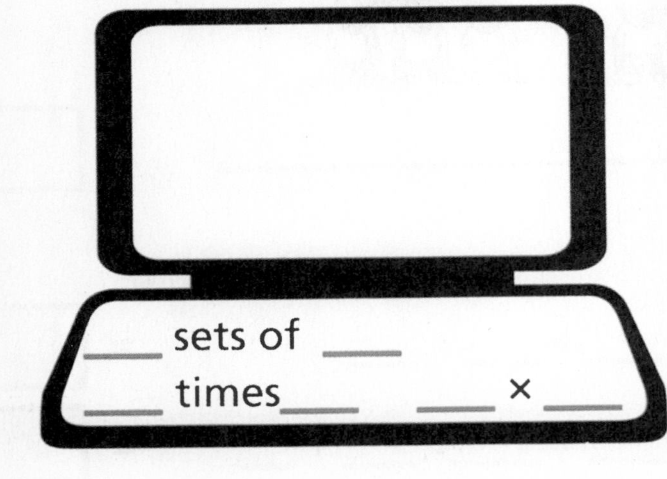

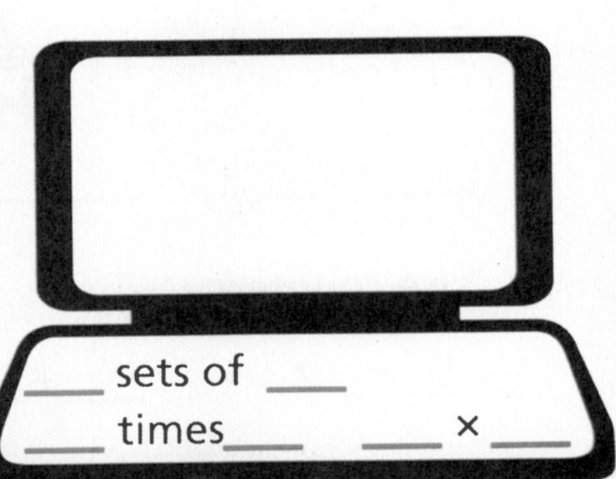

In the gym

3 sets of 5 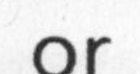 or 3 fives

3 × 5 = 5 + 5 + 5 = 15

1 Now do these.

3 fours

3 × 4 = ____ + ____ + ____ = 

5 twos

____ × ____ = ____ + ____ + ____ + ____ + ____ = 

____ threes

____ × ____ = ________________ = 

2 ________

____ × ____ = ________________ = 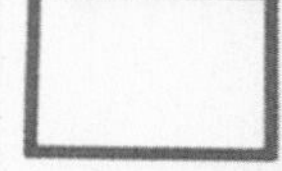

2 Use counters.

5 × 2 = ____ + ____ + ____ + ____ + ____ = ☐

6 × 3 = ____ + ____ + ____ + ____ + ____ + ____ = ☐

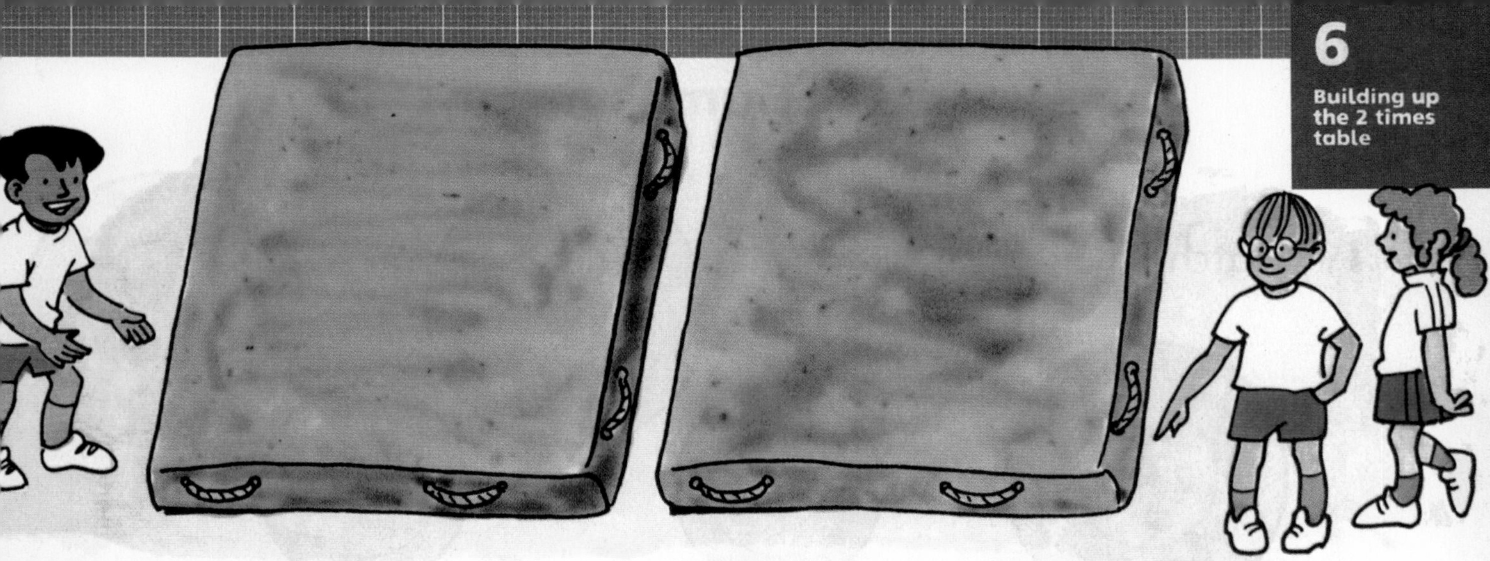

1 Put the same number of children on each mat.
Use counters.

2 × 1 = ☐ 2 × 4 = ☐ 2 × 7 = ☐

2 × 2 = ☐ 2 × 5 = ☐ 2 × 8 = ☐

2 × 3 = ☐ 2 × 6 = ☐ 2 × 9 = ☐

2 × 10 = ☐

2 Draw 5 bean bags in each hoop.

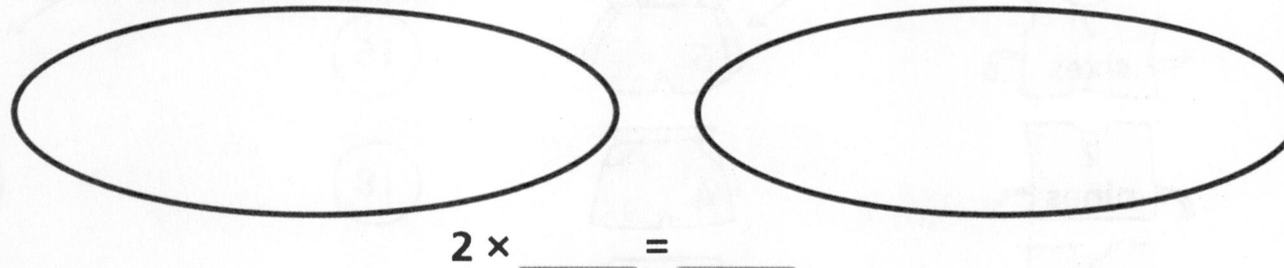

2 × ____ = ____

Draw 6 bats in each hoop.

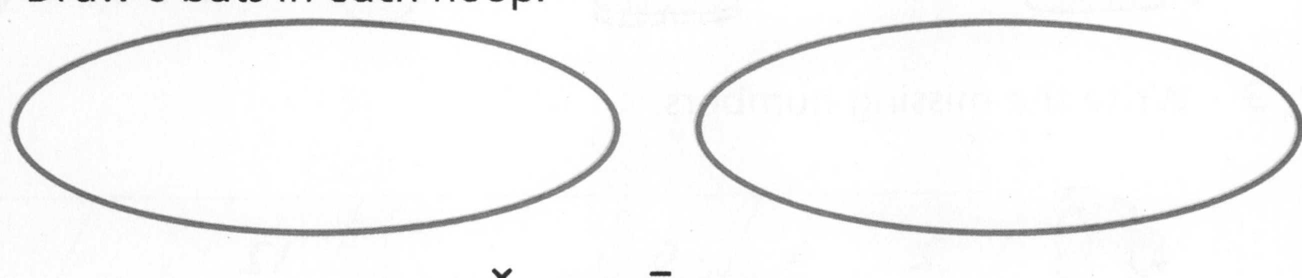

____ × ____ = ____

Draw 9 balls in each hoop.

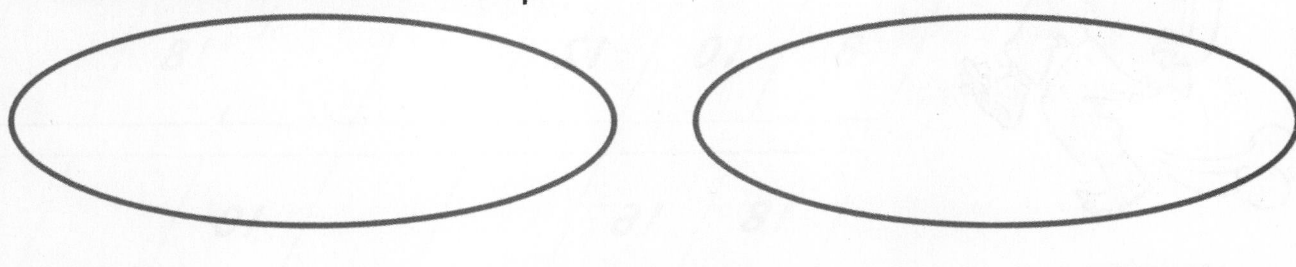

____ × ____ = ____

Games

1 Match.

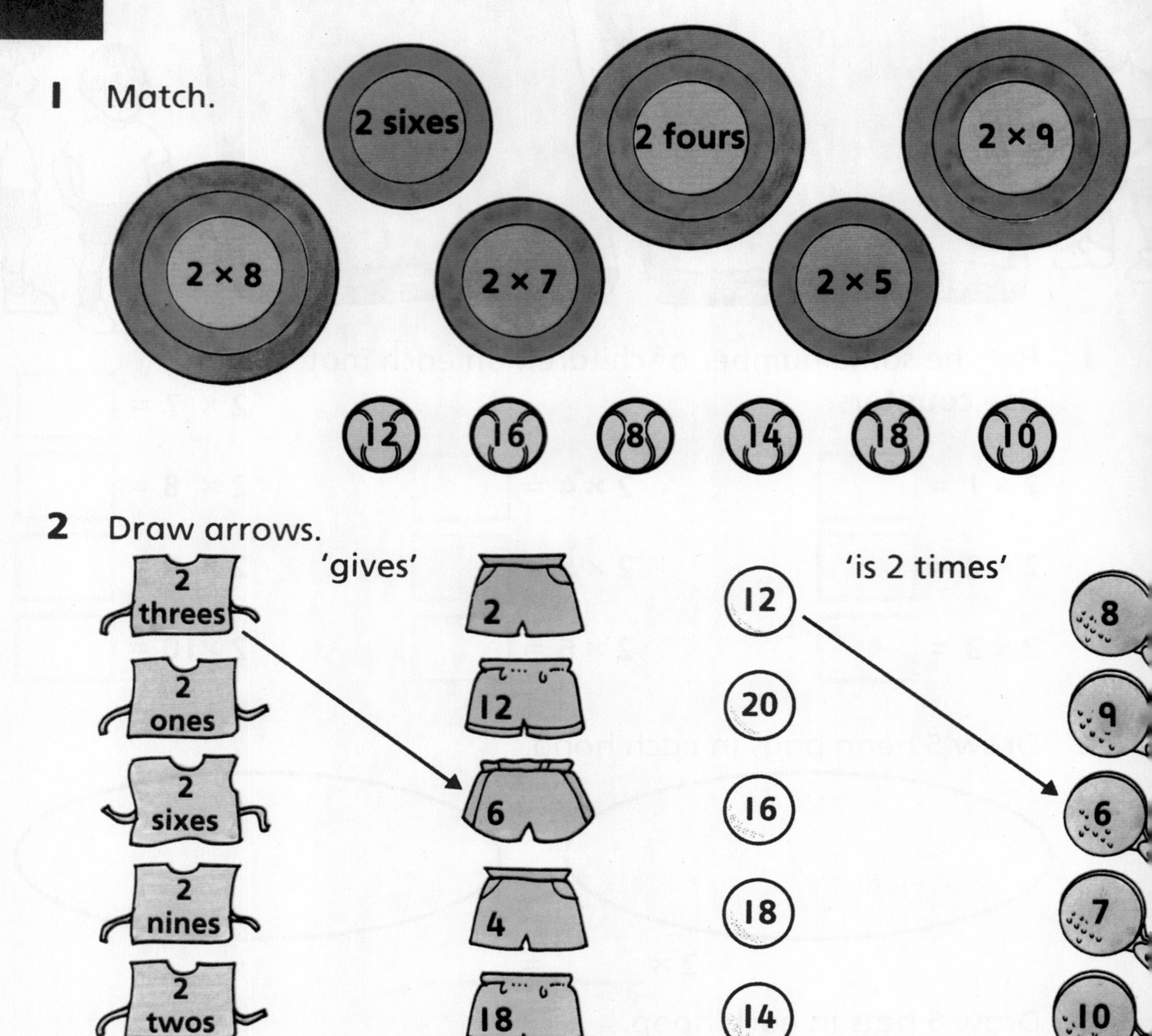

2 Draw arrows.

3 Write the missing numbers.

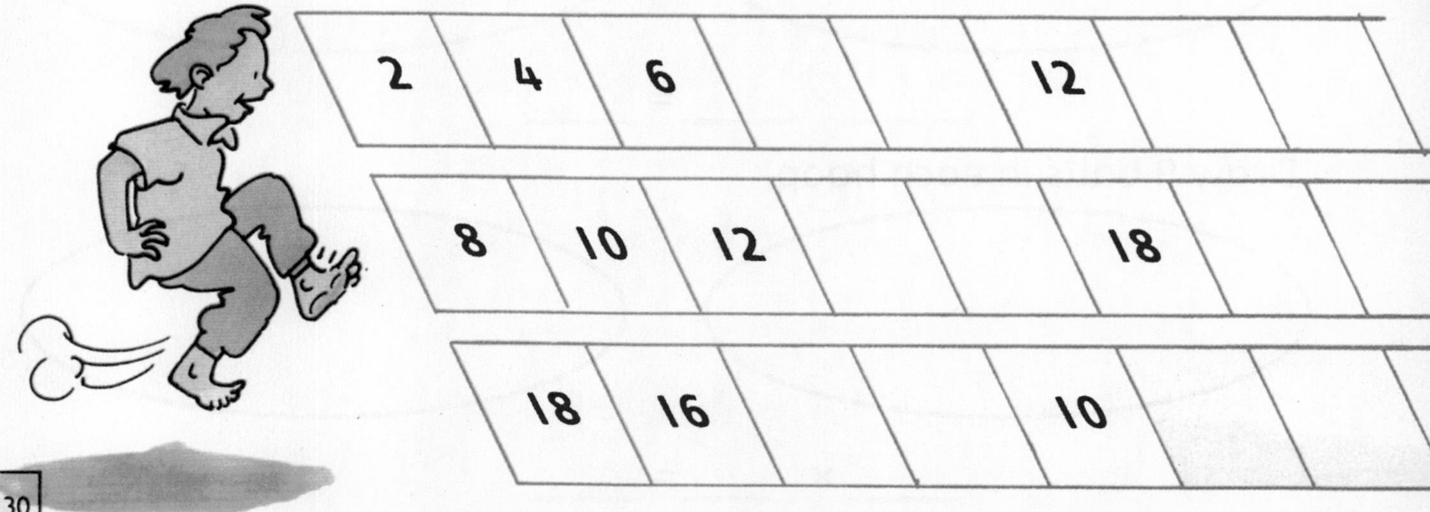

1 Match.

2 Complete.

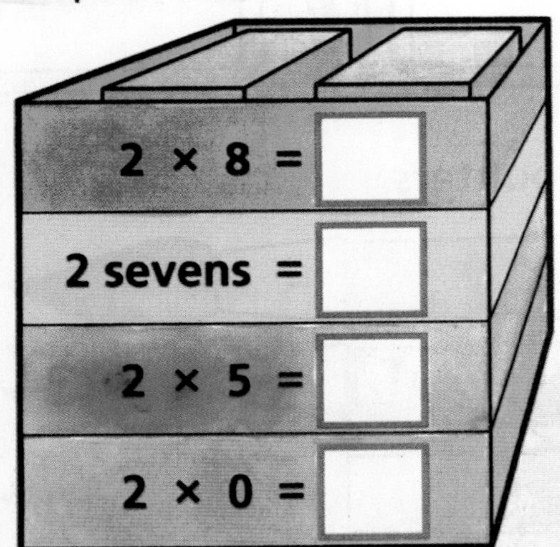

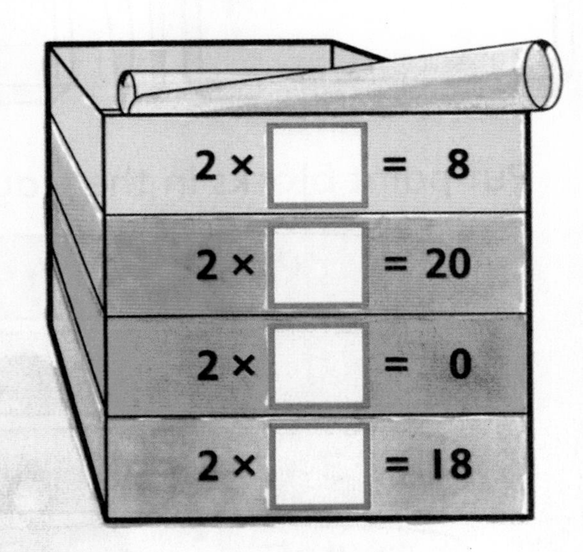

3 How many balls?

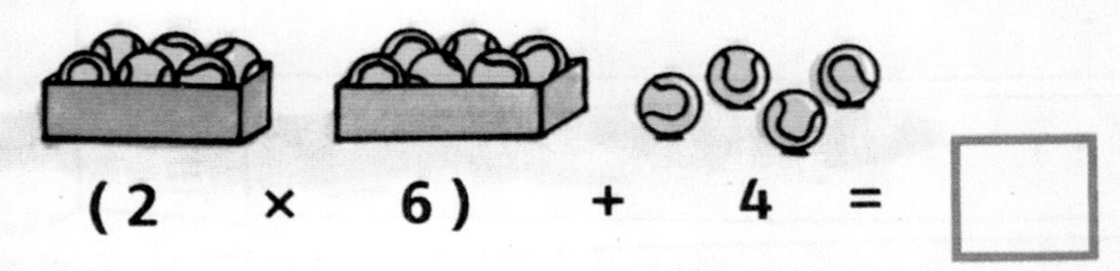

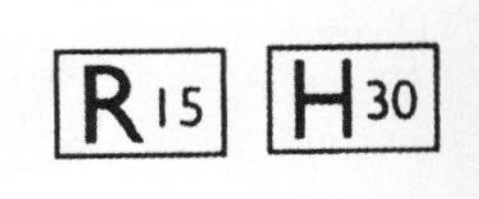

4 $(2 \times 8) + 3 = \square$ $\quad (2 \times 9) + 2 = \square$ $\quad (2 \times 7) - 5 = \square$

Extension

5 $(2 \times 6) + \square = 13$ $\quad (2 \times 0) + \square = 5$ $\quad (2 \times 10) - \square = 18$

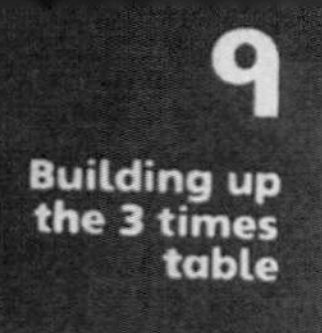

Art time

3 trays. 5 paint blocks in each.

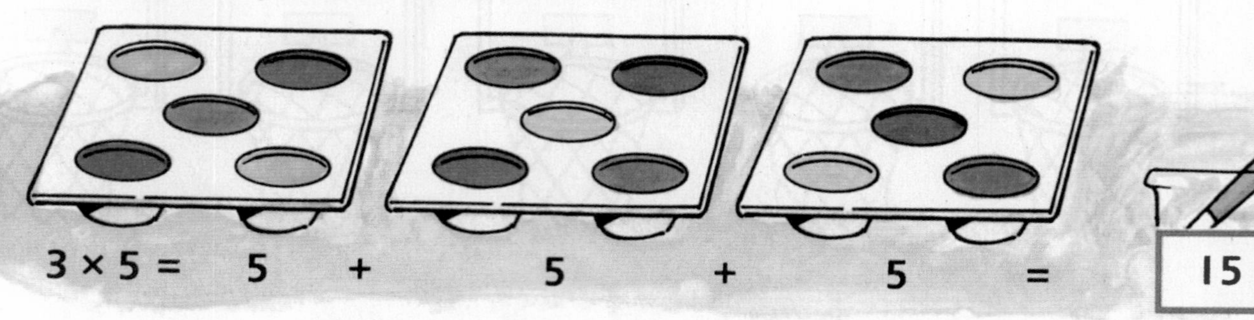

$3 \times 5 = 5 + 5 + 5 = 15$

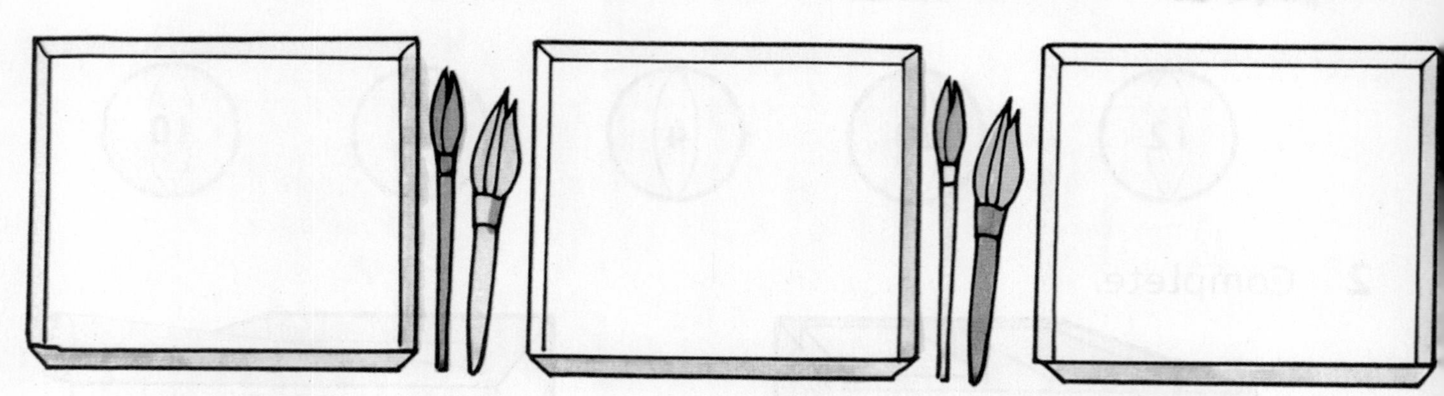

Put paint blocks in the trays. **Use counters.**

$3 \times 1 =$ ____ + ____ + ____ = ☐

$3 \times 2 =$ ____ + ____ + ____ = ☐

$3 \times 3 =$ ____ + ____ + ____ = ☐

$3 \times 4 =$ ____ + ____ + ____ = ☐

$3 \times 5 =$ = ☐

$3 \times 6 =$ = ☐

$3 \times 7 =$ = ☐

$3 \times 8 =$ = ☐

$3 \times 9 =$ = ☐

$3 \times 10 =$ = ☐

1

2 Colour to match.

3 Complete the number pattern.

4 How many crayons?

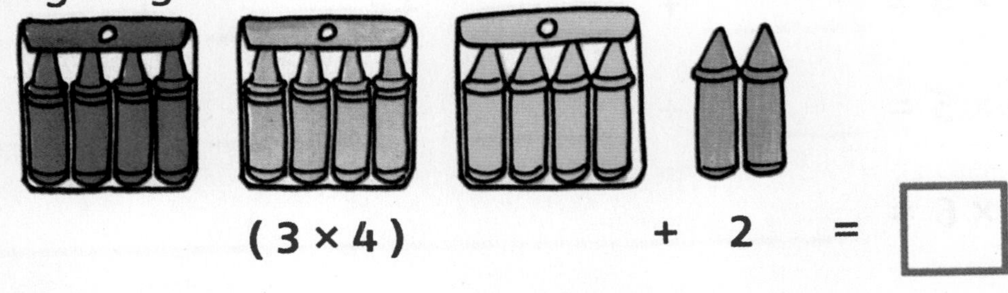

$(3 \times 4) + 2 = \square$

5 $(3 \times 3) + 4 = \square$ $(3 \times 8) - 3 = \square$ $(3 \times 0) + 5 = \square$

Extension

6 $(3 \times 2) + \square = 7$ $(3 \times 5) + \square = 17$ $(3 \times 10) - \square = 29$

Go to Textbook page 17

4 slices of cake. 5 cherries in each.

$4 \times 5 =$ 5 + 5 + 5 + 5 = 20

1 Draw cherries and write the stories.

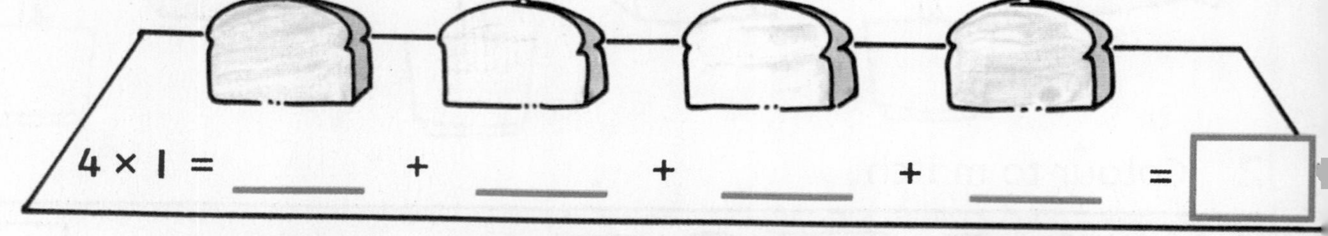

$4 \times 1 =$ ___ + ___ + ___ + ___ = ☐

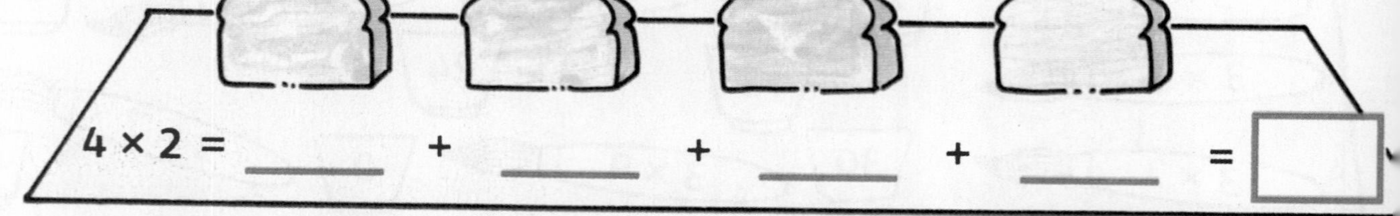

$4 \times 2 =$ ___ + ___ + ___ + ___ = ☐

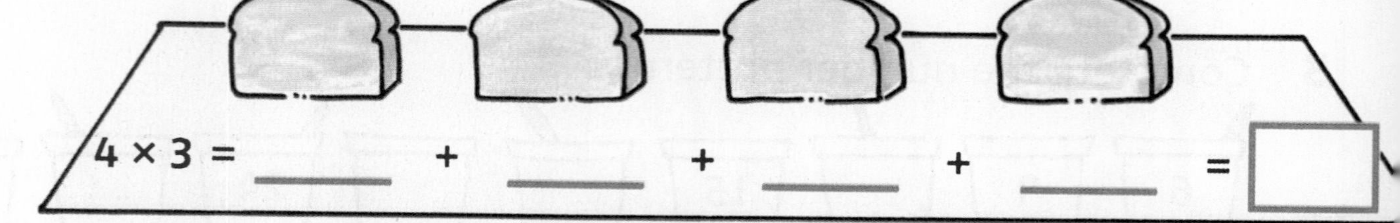

$4 \times 3 =$ ___ + ___ + ___ + ___ = ☐

2

$4 \times 4 =$ ___ + ___ + ___ + ___ = ☐

$4 \times 5 =$ ___ + ___ + ___ + ___ = ☐

$4 \times 6 =$ ________________ = ☐

$4 \times 7 =$ ________________ = ☐

$4 \times 8 =$ ________________ = ☐

$4 \times 9 =$ ________________ = ☐

$4 \times 10 =$ ________________ = ☐

Check.

1 

apples 4 × 6p = ____ p

sandwiches 4 × ____ p = ____ p

colas 4 × ____ p = ____ p

peaches ____ = ____

rolls ____ = ____

milk drinks ____ = ____

Menu

cola 9p
milk 5p
apple 6p
peach 7p
roll 8p
sandwich 10p

2 

Choose 2 fruits. ________ and ________
Buy 4 of each.
How much did you spend? ____ p

3 Colour to match.

4 Complete.

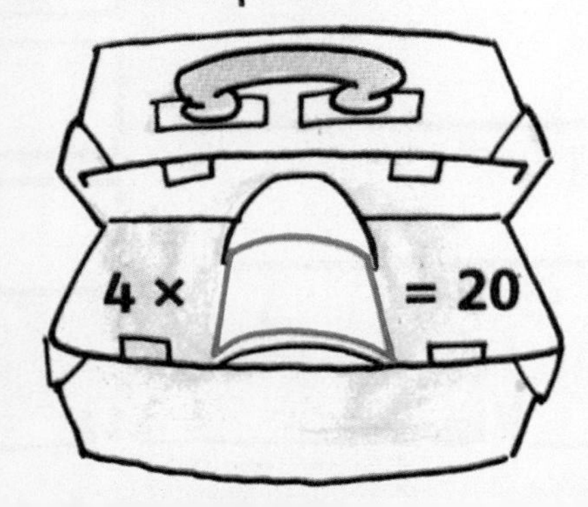

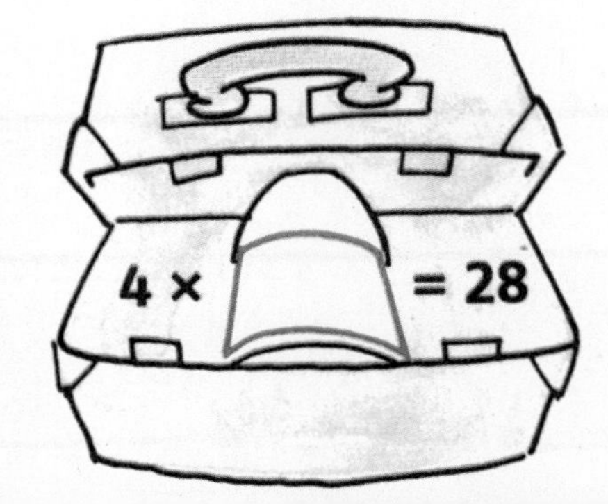

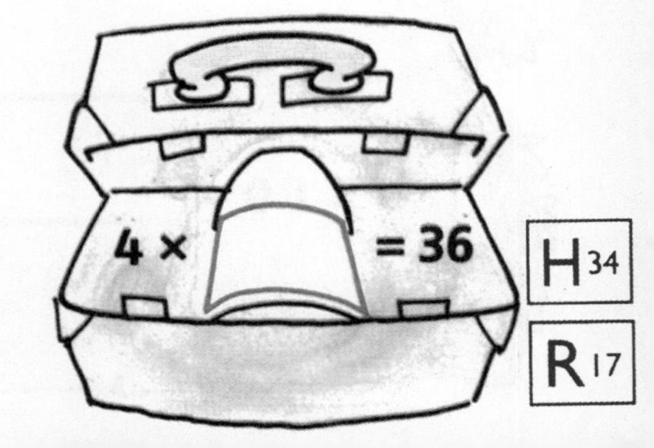

School garden

5 flower beds. 4 flowers in each.

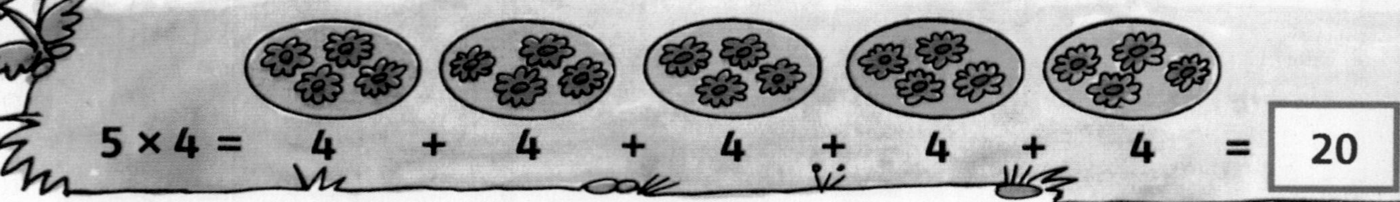

5 × 4 = 4 + 4 + 4 + 4 + 4 = 20

1 Draw flowers and write the stories.

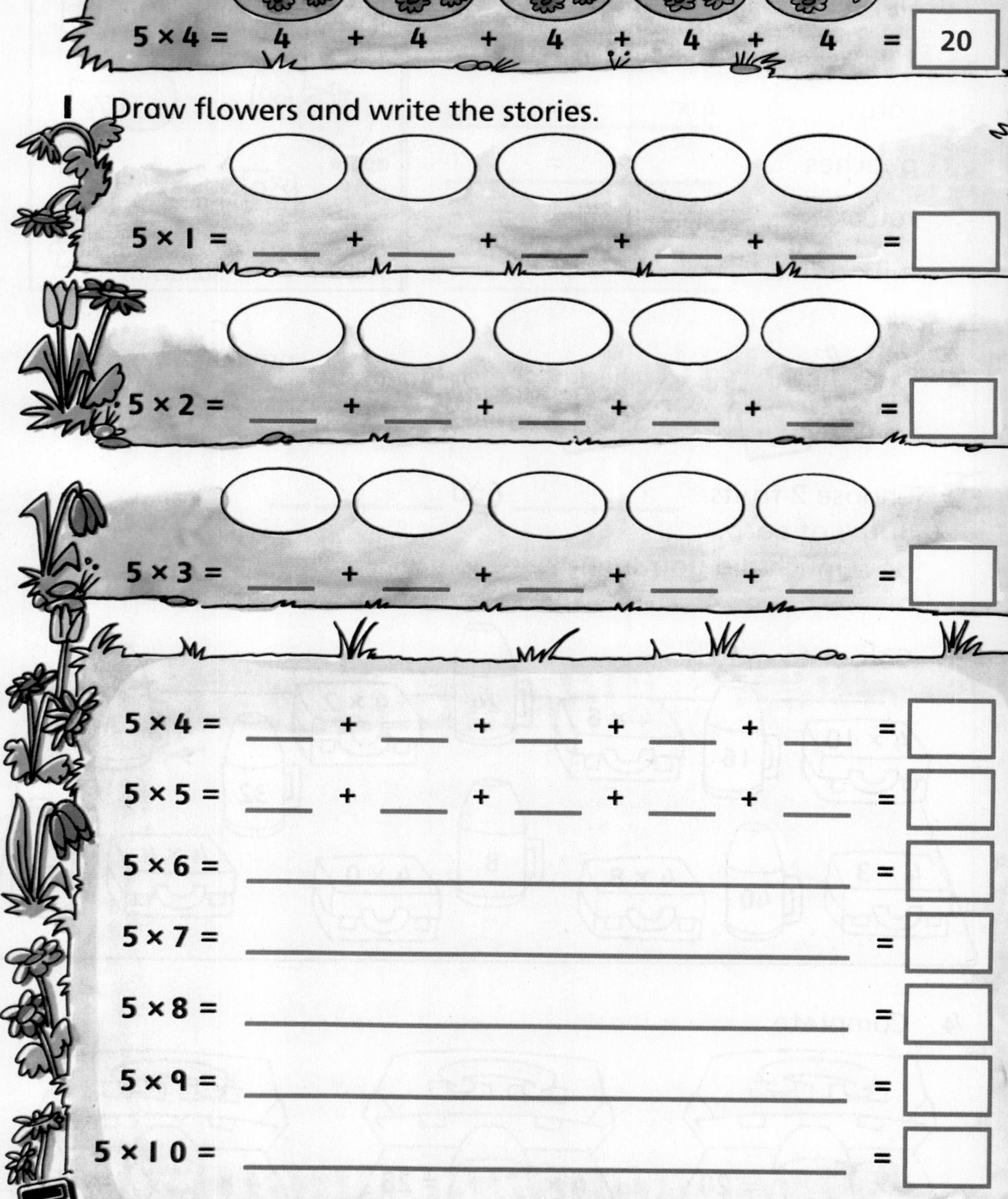

5 × 1 = ___ + ___ + ___ + ___ + ___ = [ ]

5 × 2 = ___ + ___ + ___ + ___ + ___ = [ ]

5 × 3 = ___ + ___ + ___ + ___ + ___ = [ ]

5 × 4 = ___ + ___ + ___ + ___ + ___ = [ ]

5 × 5 = ___ + ___ + ___ + ___ + ___ = [ ]

5 × 6 = ______________________ = [ ]

5 × 7 = ______________________ = [ ]

5 × 8 = ______________________ = [ ]

5 × 9 = ______________________ = [ ]

5 × 10 = ______________________ = [ ]

Check.

1 Complete.

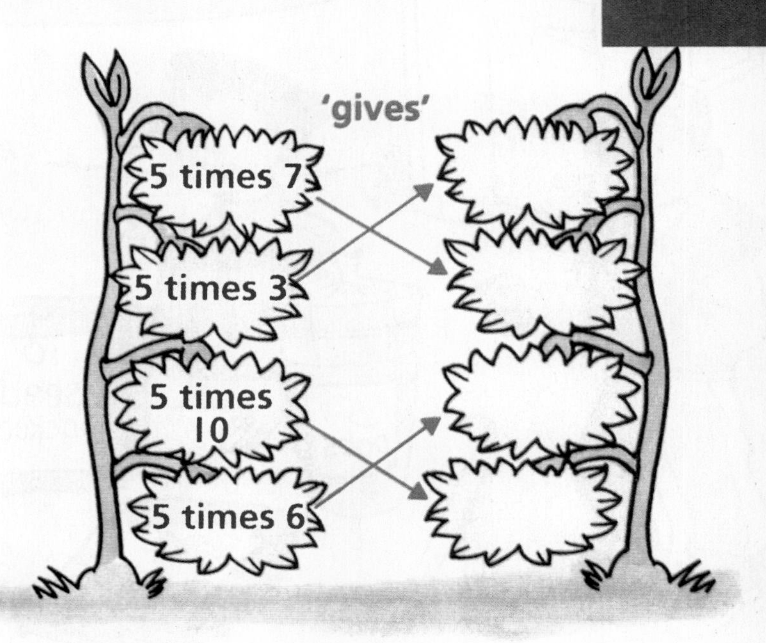

2 Colour to match.

3 Join the numbers in order.

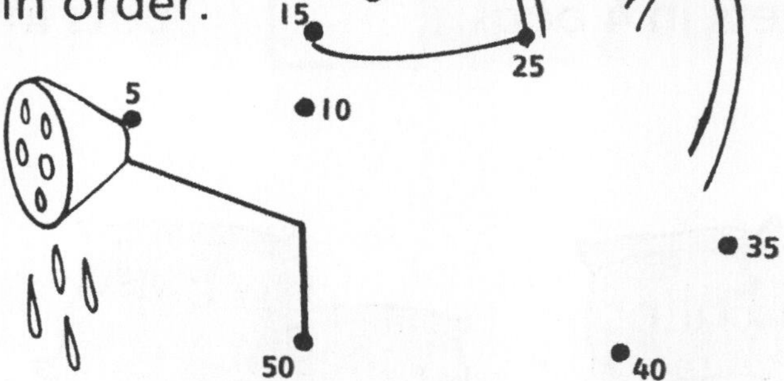

4 Write the missing numbers.

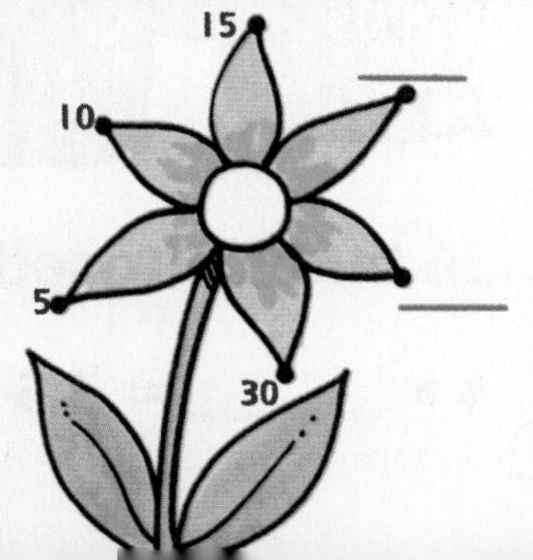

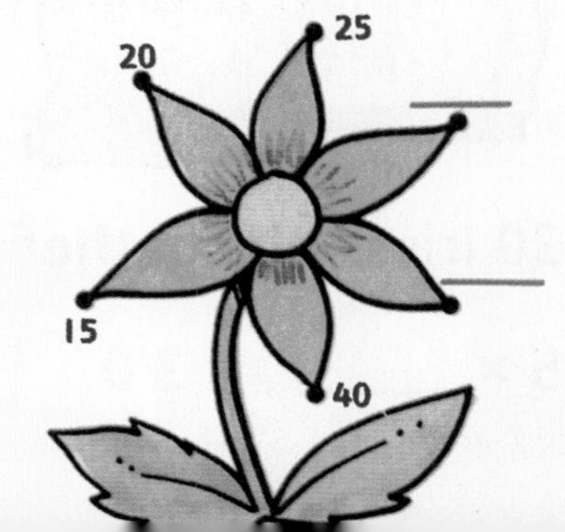

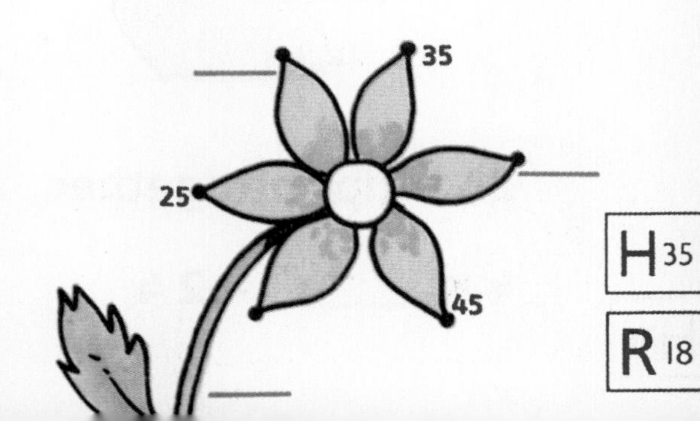

15

Using the 4 and 5 times tables

1 **How many?**

labels in 4 boxes		labels in 5 boxes	
bulbs in 4 bags		bulbs in 5 bags	
seed packets in 5 bags		canes in 4 bundles	
canes in 5 bundles		pots in 4 packs	
seed packets in 4 bags		pots in 5 packs	

2

24 tulips altogether

4 × ______ = 24

30 irises altogether

5 × ______ = 30

36 bulbs altogether

4 × ______ = 36

1 How much altogether?

5 leeks cost	____ p	4 leeks cost	____ p
4 pinks cost	____ p	5 tulips cost	____ p
Total cost	____ p	Total cost	____ p

5 pansies cost	____	4 tulips cost	____
4 lettuce cost	____	5 lettuce cost	____
Total cost	____	Total cost	____

2 How much change?

John had	50 p	Karen had	50 p
He bought 4 daisies	____ p	She bought 5 pinks	____ p
His change was	____ p	Her change was	____ p

Anna had	50 p	Winston had	50 p
She bought 5 daisies	____	He bought 4 pansies	____
Her change was	____	His change was	____

School library

5 twos  5 × 2 = 10

2 fives  2 × 5 = 10

5 × 2 = 2 × 5

1 Colour 2 fours  2 × 4 = ____

4 twos  4 × 2 = ____

× = ×

Colour 5 threes  5 × 3 = ____

3 fives 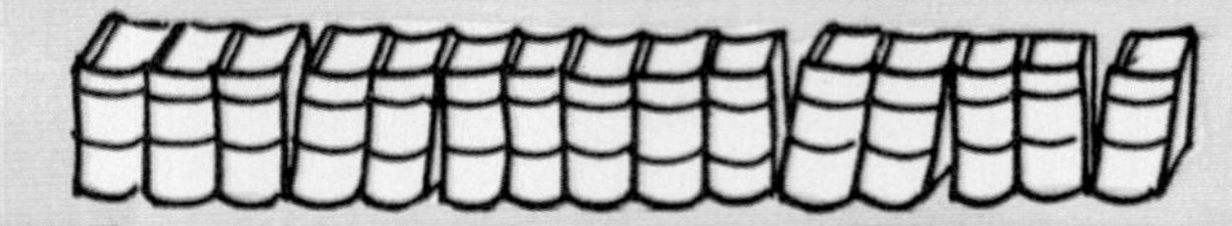 3 × 5 = ____

× = ×

2 2 threes 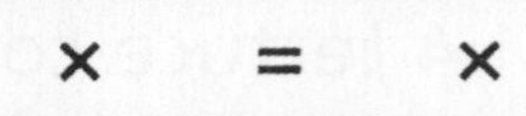 2 × 3 = 6

0 1 2 3 4 5 6 7 8 9 10 11 12 13 14

Draw

3 twos

0 1 2 3 4 5 6 7 8 9 10 11 12 13 14

3 × 2 = ____

× = ×

Draw

3 fours

0 1 2 3 4 5 6 7 8 9 10 11 12 13 14

3 × 4 = ____

4 threes 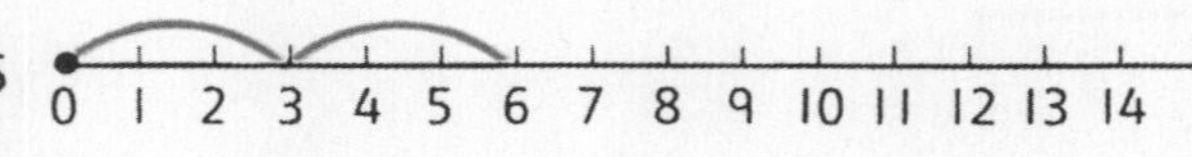

0 1 2 3 4 5 6 7 8 9 10 11 12 13 14

4 × 3 = ____

× = ×

1

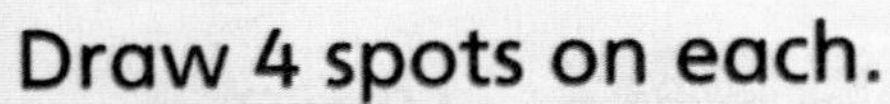

Draw 2 spots on each.

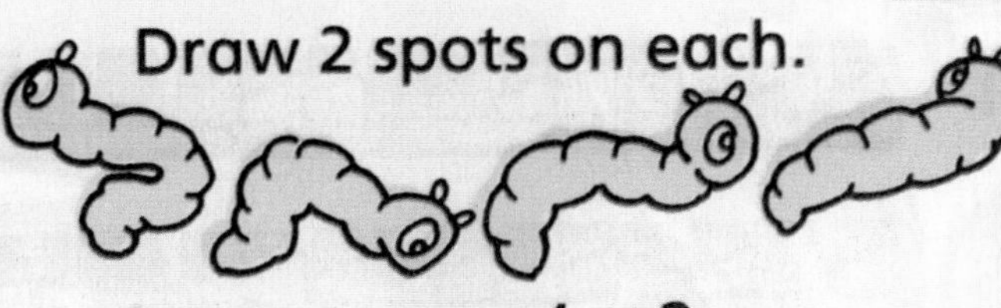

2 × 4 = ____ 4 × 2 = ____

× = ×

Draw 5 spots on each.

4 × 5 = ____

Draw 4 spots on each.

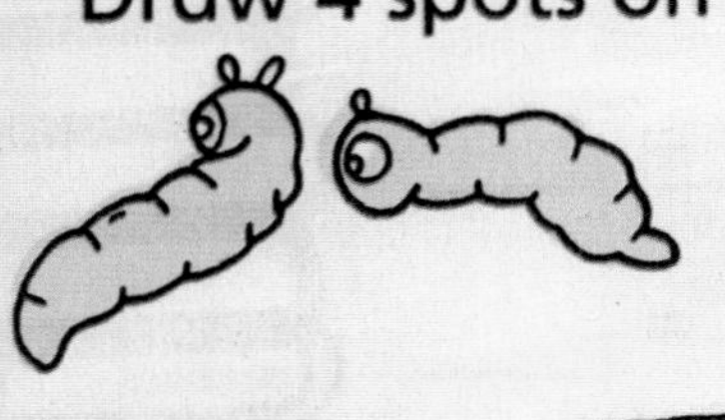

5 × 4 = ____

× = ×

2 Match the boxes.

Check.

3 What number is missing from the label?

____

Check.

Library tickets

1

$10 \times 2 =$ ______

$2 \times 10 =$ ______

$10 \times 2 = 2 \times 10 = 2$ tens $= 20$

2

$10 \times 1 = 1 \times 10 = 1$ ten $= 10$

$10 \times 2 = 2 \times 10 = 2$ tens $= 20$

$10 \times 3 = 3 \times 10 = 3$ tens $=$ ___

$10 \times 4 = 4 \times 10 = 4$ tens $=$ ___

$10 \times 5 =$ ______ $=$ ___ tens $=$ ___

$10 \times 6 =$ ______ $=$ ___ tens $=$ ___

$10 \times 7 =$ ______ $=$ ___ tens $=$ ___

$10 \times 8 =$ ______ $=$ ___ tens $=$ ___

$10 \times 9 =$ ______ $=$ ___ tens $=$ ___

$10 \times 10 =$ ______ $=$ ___ tens $= 100$

10 tens = 1 hundred = 100

3 How many tickets are in each box?

$(10 \times 5) + 3 =$ ______

$(10 \times 7) + 2 =$ ______

$(10 \times 4) - 2 =$ ______

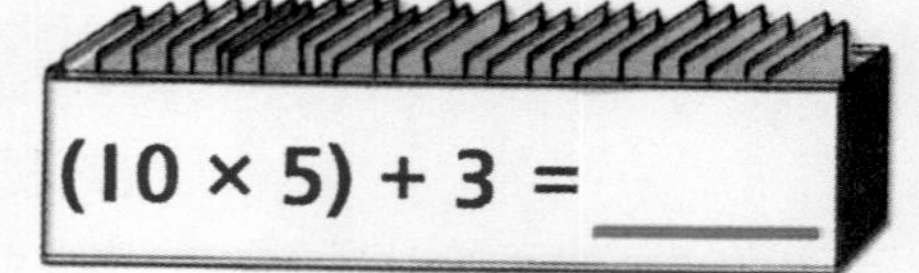

$10 \times 10 =$ ______

$(10 \times 0) + 8 =$ ______

$(10 \times 9) + 10 =$ ______

Book sale

You can buy the books with these coins.

Ten 10p coins can be changed for 
$10 \times 10p = 100p = £1$

1 Find how much money each boy has.

   ______ p

      ______ p

    ______ p

2 Can each buy a bundle of books? ______

3 Draw coins to show other ways of paying for the books.

Catching the bus

1 Put answers less than 40 downstairs.
Put answers greater than 40 upstairs.

2

Joan has twice as many as Leela. How many has Joan? ______

Peter has 3 times as many as Leela. How many has Peter? ______

Jean has 4 times as many as Leela. How many has Jean? ______

1 Find the cost of

2 tennis racquets £ ______ 4 bags £ ______

10 T-shirts ______ 10 sports skirts ______

3 footballs ______ 5 skirts and 5 shirts ______

Extension

2 Find the total cost of 2 of each item.
Find the total cost of 4 of each item.
The school has £100. Can it buy 5 of each item?

3 Children live in the flats where the answers are less than 20. Colour their windows.

4 In the car park, colour the **even** answers red and the **odd** answers green.

5 × 3) + 2	(4 × 9) + 4	(10 × 5) + 6	(2 × 9) + 3	(3 × 7) + 3	(5 × 5) + 5
×6) − 5	(3 × 9) − 10	(5 × 8) − 2	(10 × 10) − 9	(4 × 8) − 6	(2 × 8) − 3

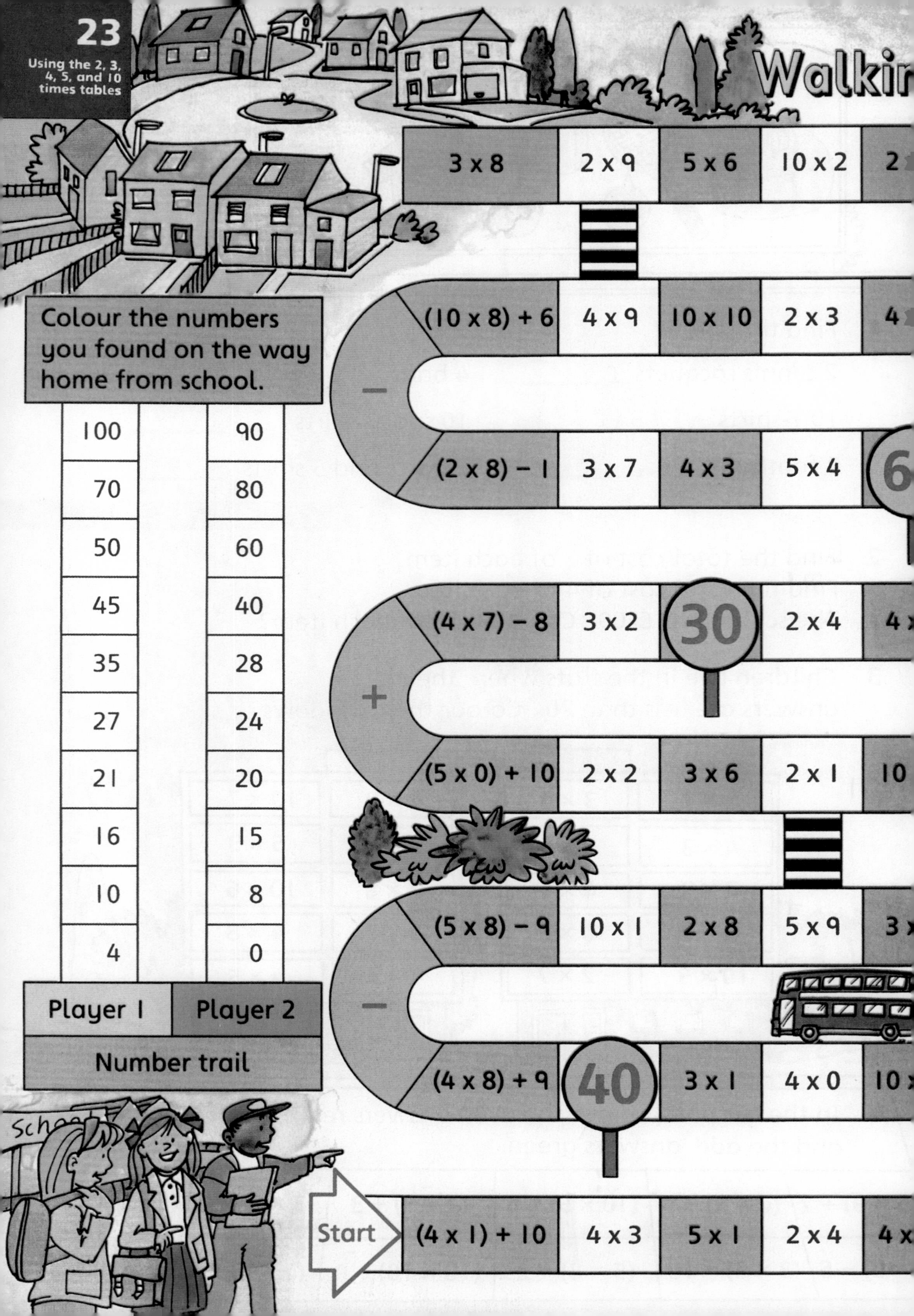
23
Using the 2, 3, 4, 5, and 10 times tables
Walkir
Colour the numbers you found on the way home from school.
100
90
70
80
50
60
45
40
35
28
27
24
21
20
16
15
10
8
4
0
Player 1
Player 2
Number trail
Start
(4 x 1) + 10
4 x 3
5 x 1
2 x 4
4 x
(4 x 8) + 9
40
3 x 1
4 x 0
10 x
−
(5 x 8) − 9
10 x 1
2 x 8
5 x 9
3 x
(5 x 0) + 10
2 x 2
3 x 6
2 x 1
10
+
(4 x 7) − 8
3 x 2
30
2 x 4
4 x
(2 x 8) − 1
3 x 7
4 x 3
5 x 4
6
−
(10 x 8) + 6
4 x 9
10 x 10
2 x 3
4
3 x 8
2 x 9
5 x 6
10 x 2
2
Scho

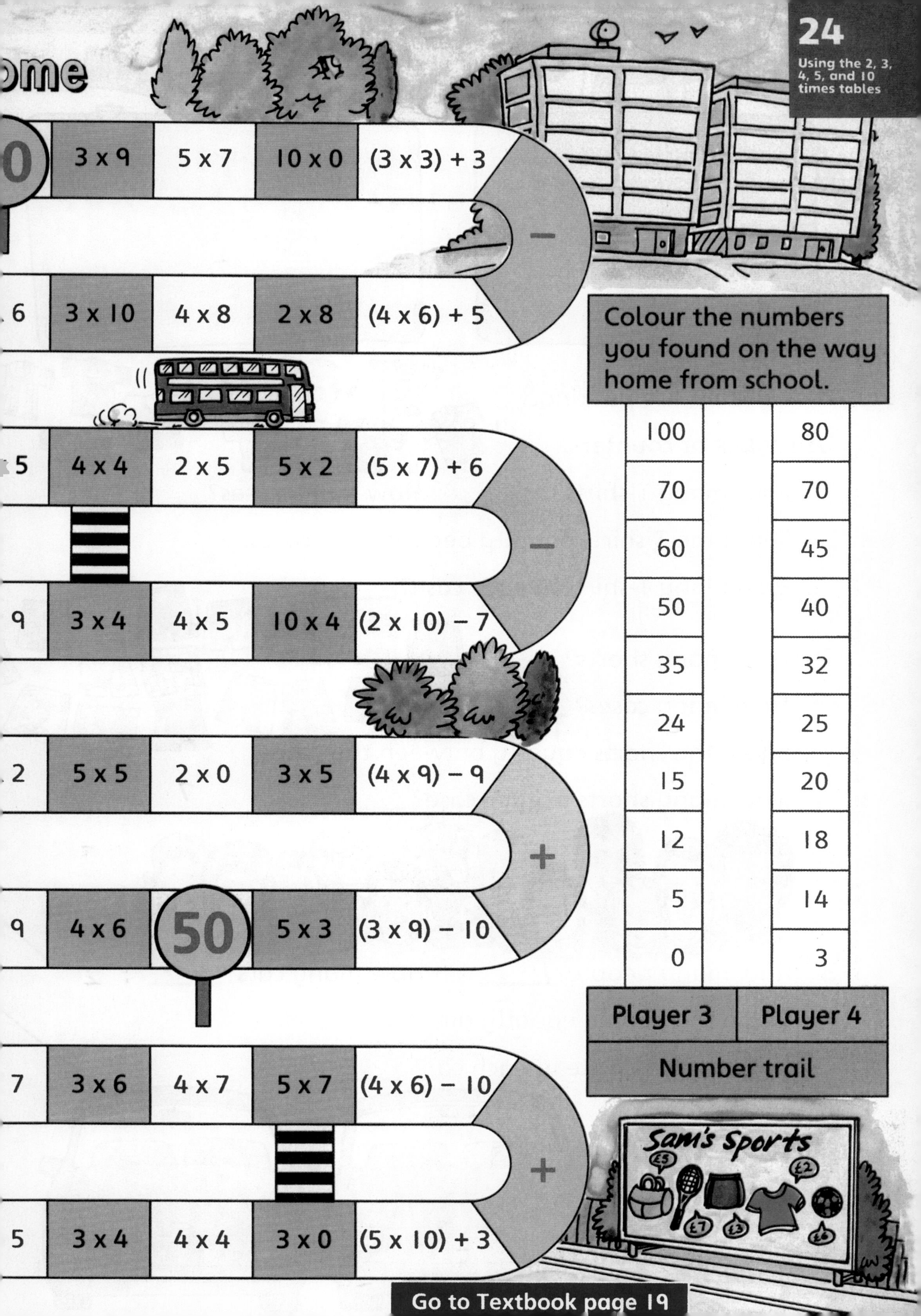

ome
24
Using the 2, 3, 4, 5, and 10 times tables
0
3 x 9
5 x 7
10 x 0
(3 x 3) + 3
−
6
3 x 10
4 x 8
2 x 8
(4 x 6) + 5
5
4 x 4
2 x 5
5 x 2
(5 x 7) + 6
−
9
3 x 4
4 x 5
10 x 4
(2 x 10) − 7
2
5 x 5
2 x 0
3 x 5
(4 x 9) − 9
+
9
4 x 6
50
5 x 3
(3 x 9) − 10
7
3 x 6
4 x 7
5 x 7
(4 x 6) − 10
+
5
3 x 4
4 x 4
3 x 0
(5 x 10) + 3
Colour the numbers you found on the way home from school.
100
70
60
50
35
24
15
12
5
0
80
70
45
40
32
25
20
18
14
3
Player 3
Player 4
Number trail
Sam's Sports
£5
£2
£7
£3
£6
Go to Textbook page 19

ON HOLIDAY

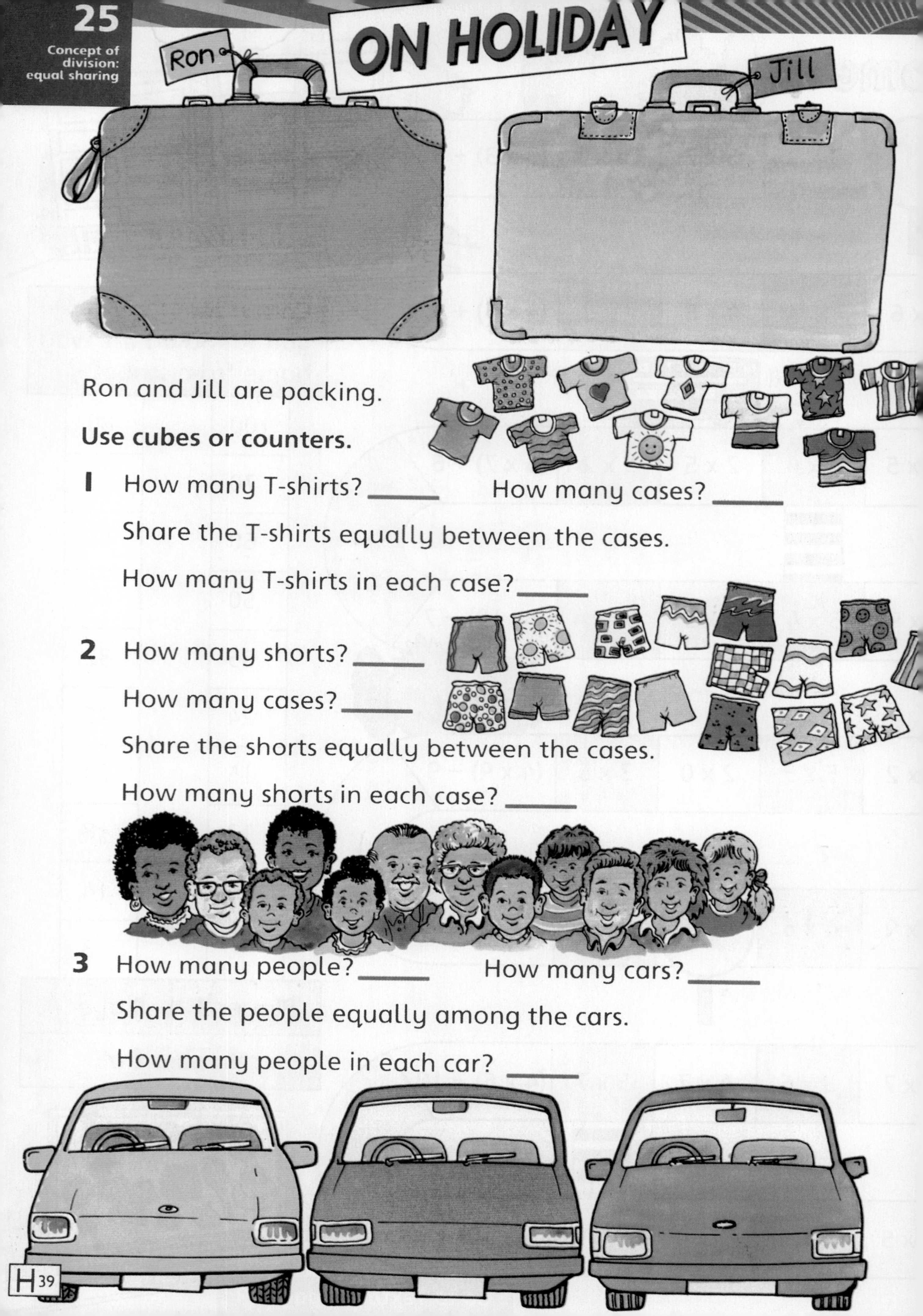

Ron and Jill are packing.

Use cubes or counters.

1 How many T-shirts? ______ How many cases? ______

Share the T-shirts equally between the cases.

How many T-shirts in each case? ______

2 How many shorts? ______

How many cases? ______

Share the shorts equally between the cases.

How many shorts in each case? ______

3 How many people? ______ How many cars? ______

Share the people equally among the cars.

How many people in each car? ______

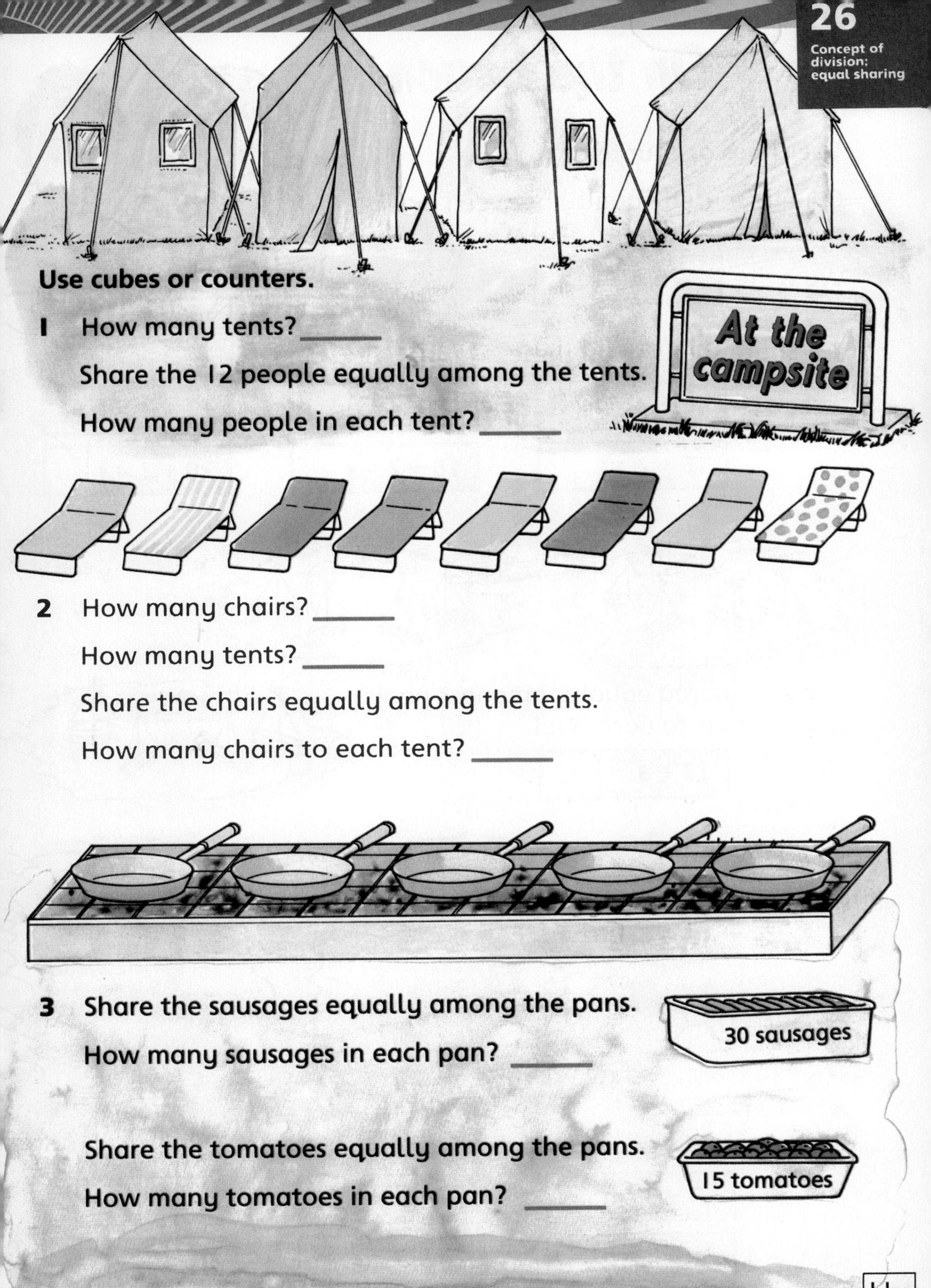

Use cubes or counters.

1 How many tents? ______

Share the 12 people equally among the tents.

How many people in each tent? ______

2 How many chairs? ______

How many tents? ______

Share the chairs equally among the tents.

How many chairs to each tent? ______

3 Share the sausages equally among the pans.

How many sausages in each pan? ______

Share the tomatoes equally among the pans.

How many tomatoes in each pan? ______

27
Division: sharing using the ÷ sign

On the beach

Use cubes or counters.

6 shells shared equally between 2 girls gives 3 shells to each.

We write $6 \div 2 = 3$

1 Share shells to do these.

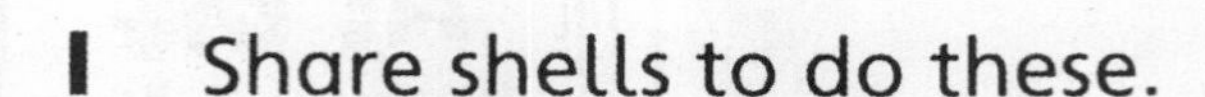

$8 \div 2 =$ ☐	$10 \div 2 =$ ☐	$12 \div 2 =$ ☐
$16 \div 2 =$ ☐	$18 \div 2 =$ ☐	$20 \div 2 =$ ☐

12 boats shared equally among 3 pools gives 4 boats to each pool.

We write $12 \div 3 = 4$

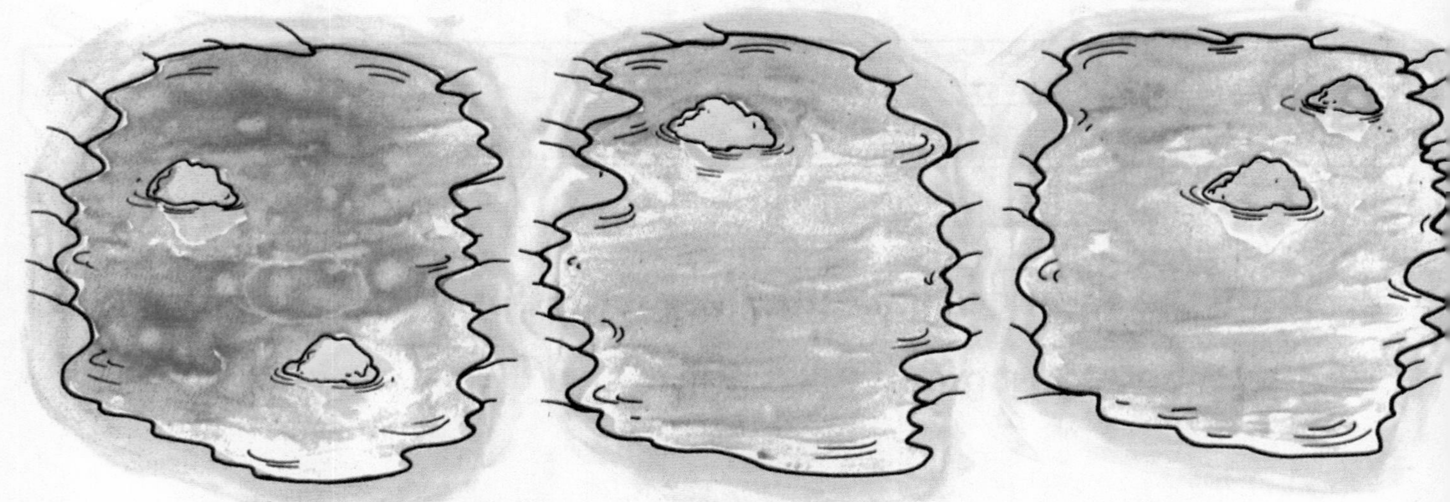

2 Share boats equally among 3 pools.

$9 \div 3 =$ ☐	$15 \div 3 =$ ☐	$18 \div 3 =$ ☐
$21 \div 3 =$ ☐	$24 \div 3 =$ ☐	$30 \div 3 =$ ☐

1 12 people shared equally among 4 umbrellas gives _____ people to each umbrella.

$12 \div 4 =$	

2 Share people equally among 4 umbrellas.

$8 \div 4 =$		$16 \div 4 =$		$20 \div 4 =$	
$24 \div 4 =$		$28 \div 4 =$		$32 \div 4 =$	

3 15 rolls shared equally among 5 plates gives _____ rolls to each plate.

$15 \div 5 =$	

4 Share rolls equally among 5 plates.

$10 \div 5 =$		$20 \div 5 =$		$25 \div 5 =$	
$30 \div 5 =$		$35 \div 5 =$		$40 \div 5 =$	

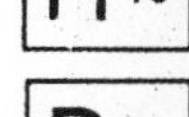

R20

5 $14 \div 2 =$ _____ $27 \div 3 =$ _____ $36 \div 4 =$ _____

$5 \div 5 =$ _____ $40 \div 4 =$ _____ $45 \div 5 =$ _____

Boating

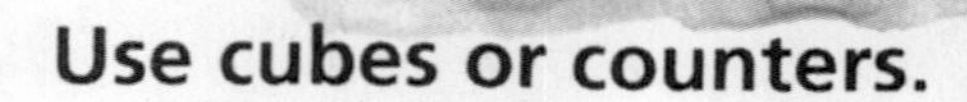

Use cubes or counters.

1 Share 13 children equally among 3 boats.

How many in each boat? 4

How many left over? 1

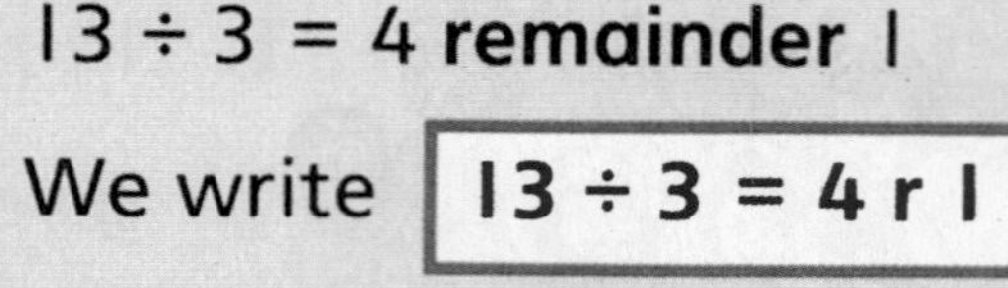

13 ÷ 3 = 4 **remainder** 1

We write **13 ÷ 3 = 4 r 1**

2 Share among 3 boats.

10 ÷ 3 = 3 r 1

11 ÷ 3 = 3 r 2

7 ÷ 3 = 2 r 1

14 ÷ 3 = 4 r 2

3 Now do these.

9 ÷ 2 = 4 r 1

13 ÷ 4 = 3 r 1

11 ÷ 4 = 2 r 3

15 ÷ 2 = 7 r 1

11 ÷ 5 = 2 r 1

13 ÷ 5 = 2 r 3

17 ÷ 5 = 3 r 2

20 ÷ 4 = 5 r 0

21 ÷ 5 = 4 r 1

17 ÷ 3 = 5 r 2

4 Match if the remainder is 1.

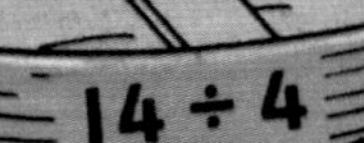

12 ÷ 3

1

10 people shared equally between 2 boats. | **10 ÷ 2 =** 20

2 lots of 5 people | **2 × 5 =** 10

2

12 people shared equally among 3 boats | **12 ÷** 3 **=** 4

3 lots of 4 people | **3 ×** 4 **=** 12

3

8 people shared equally among 4 boats | 8 **÷** 4 **=** 2

4 lots of 2 people | 4 **×** 2 **=** 8

4

15 people shared equally among 5 boats | 15 **÷** 5 **=** 3

5 lots of 3 people | 5 **×** 3 **=** 15

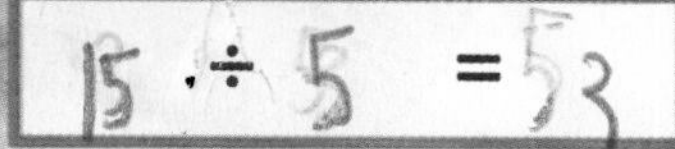

5 Draw a picture of 6 people shared equally between 2 boats.

Copy and complete: 12 **÷** 6 **=** 2 and 6 **×** 2 **=** 12

Go to Textbook page 22

Sandwiches

1 Ron cut his sandwich into two equal parts.

What is each part called? half

We write one half as $\frac{1}{2}$

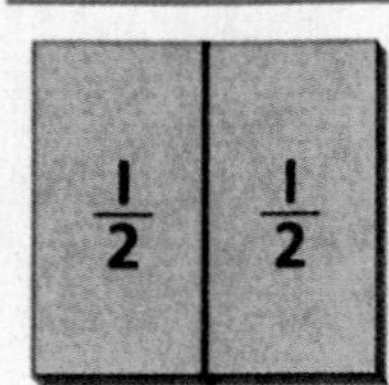

2 Tick sandwiches with two equal parts.
Write $\frac{1}{2}$ on each half.

  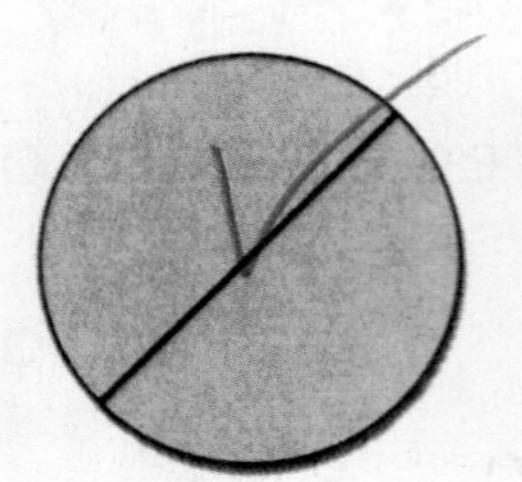 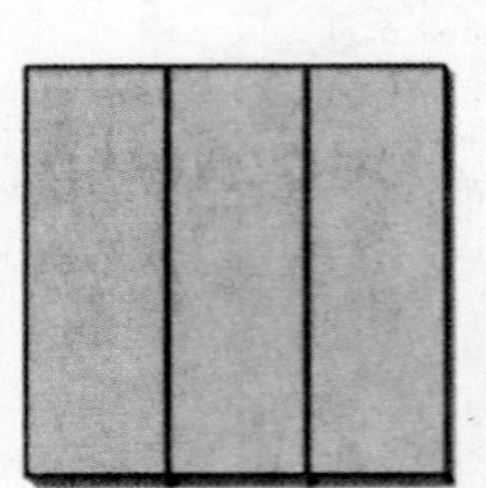 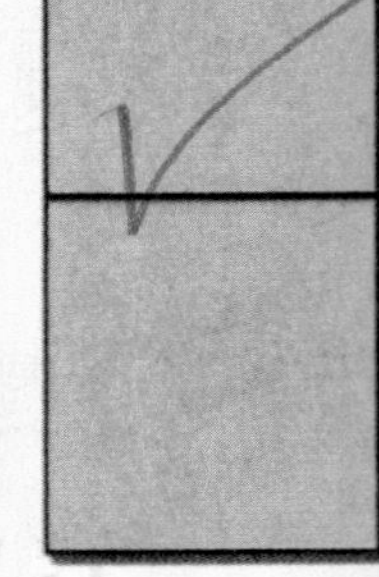

3 Jill cut her sandwiches into four equal parts.

What is each part called? quater

We write one quarter as $\frac{1}{4}$

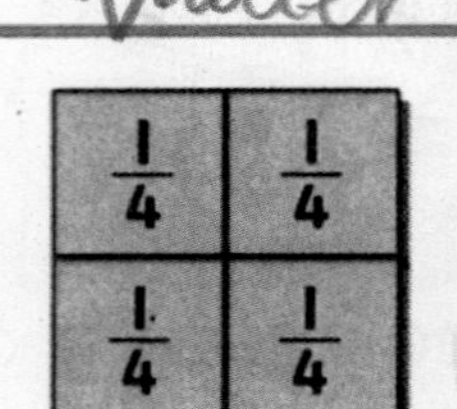

4 Tick the sandwiches with four equal parts.
Write $\frac{1}{4}$ on each quarter.

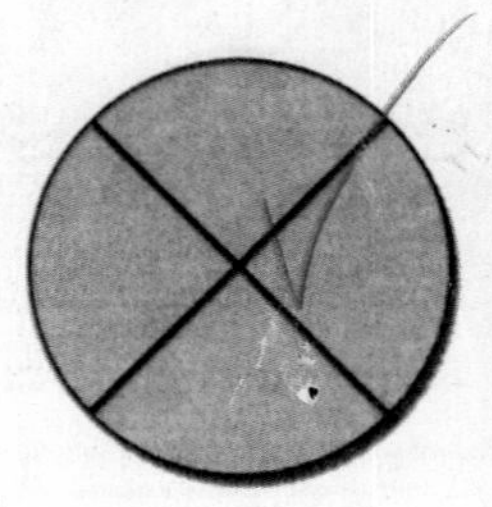  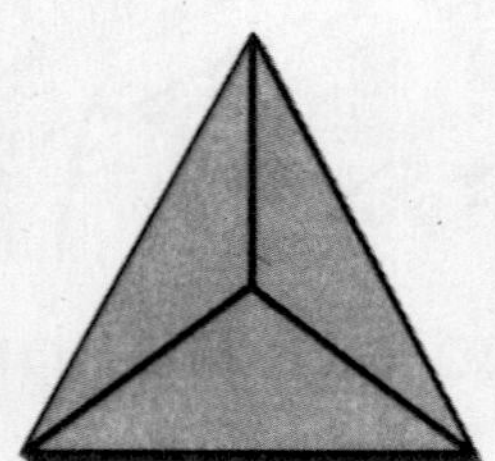  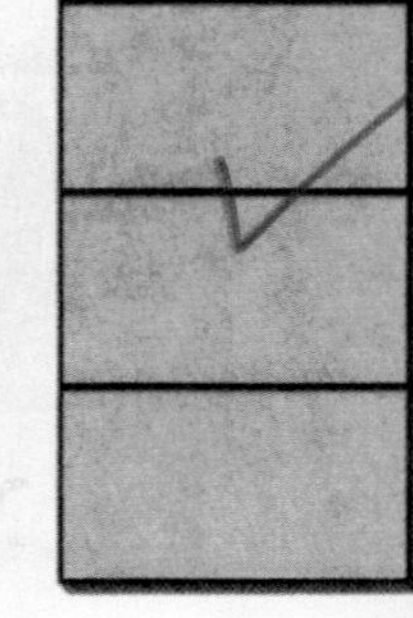

5 Write $\frac{1}{2}$ or $\frac{1}{4}$ on each part of these sandwiches.

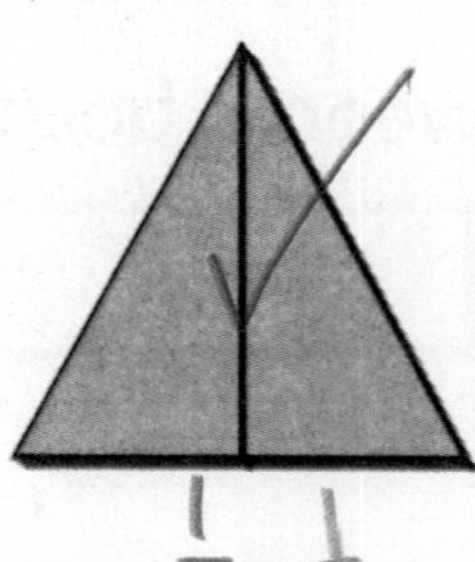 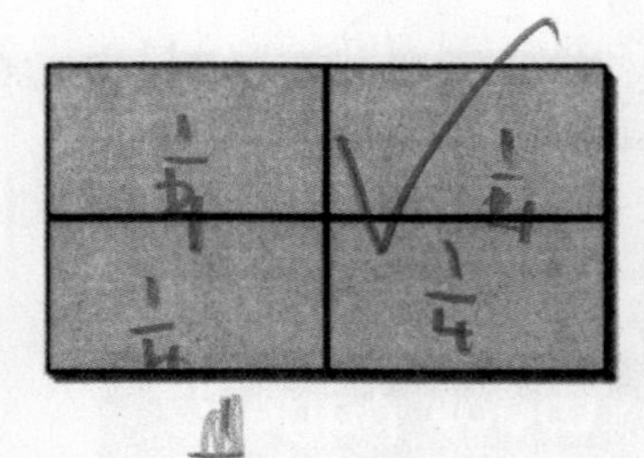 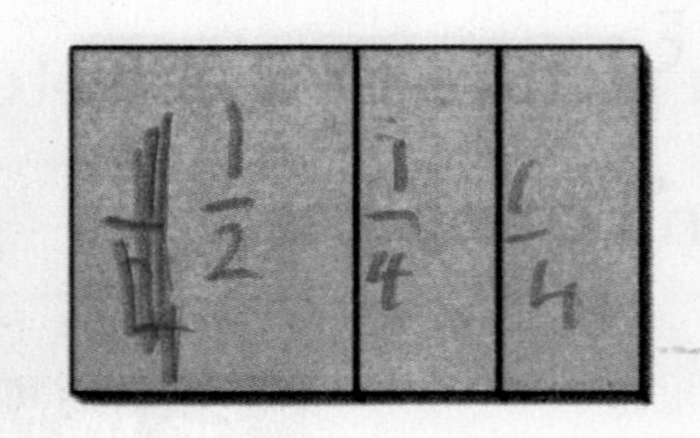 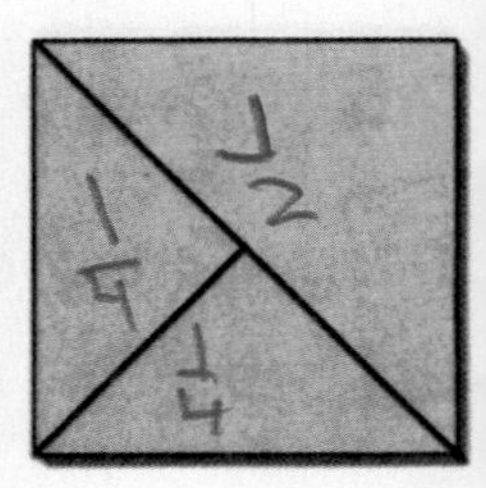

Biscuits

Two halves make one whole

Four quarters make one whole

1 Colour 1 half 2 halves

We write $\frac{1}{2}$ We write $\frac{2}{2}$

2 Colour
1 quarter 2 quarters 3 quarters 4 quarters

We write $\frac{1}{4}$ We write $\frac{2}{4}$ We write $\frac{3}{4}$ We write $\frac{4}{4}$

3 All these biscuits have **equal parts.**

Colour $\frac{1}{2}$ Colour $\frac{1}{4}$ Colour $\frac{3}{4}$ Colour $\frac{2}{2}$

4 What fraction of each biscuit is shaded?

$\frac{1}{2}$ $\frac{1}{4}$ $\frac{3}{4}$ $\frac{4}{4}=1$ $\frac{1}{2}$

$\frac{4}{4}=1$ $\frac{1}{2}$ $\frac{2}{2}=1$ $\frac{1}{2}$ $\frac{3}{4}$

The beach shop

This sheet of 12 stamps is halved.

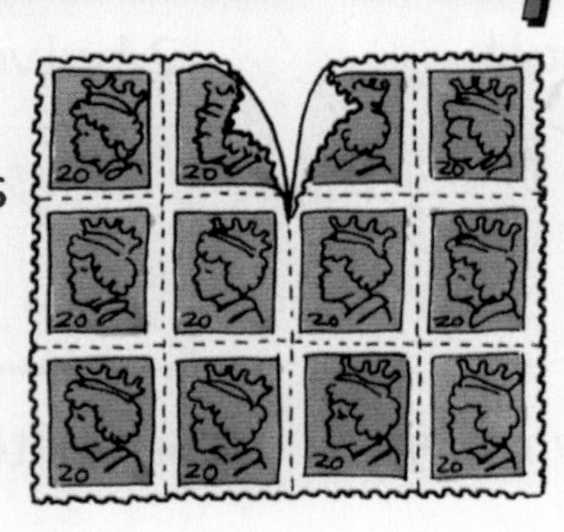

$\frac{1}{2}$ of 12 = 6

1

$\frac{1}{2}$ of 4 = 2　　$\frac{1}{2}$ of 18 = 9　　$\frac{1}{2}$ of 16 = 8

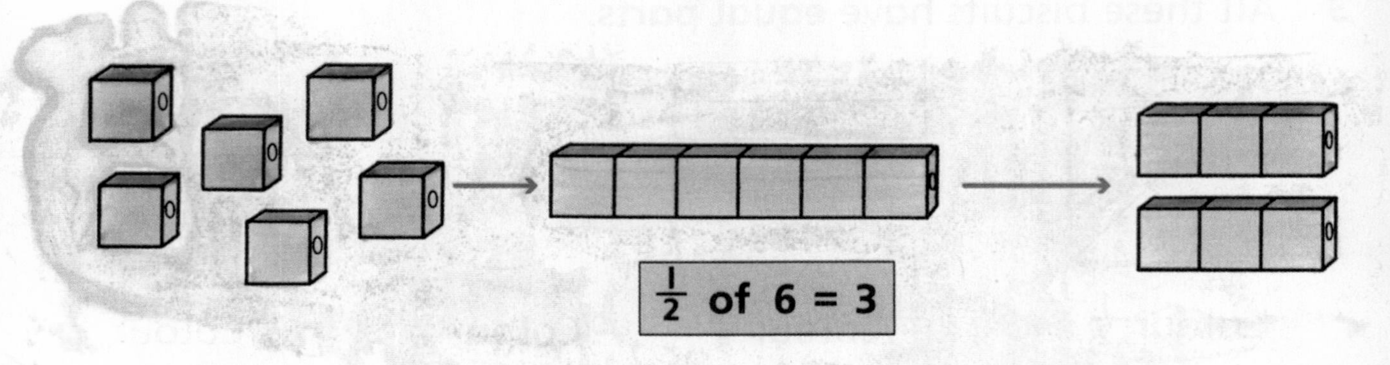

$\frac{1}{2}$ of 6 = 3

Use cubes.

2　$\frac{1}{2}$ of 8 = 4　　$\frac{1}{2}$ of 12 = 6　　$\frac{1}{2}$ of 10 = 5

3 Sue had 14 stamps. She gave half of the stamps to Sally.
Sally got 7 stamps.

4 Sally had 20 postcards. She gave half of the postcards to Sue.
Sue got 10 postcards.

This tray of 20 badges is quartered.

$\frac{1}{4}$ of 20 = 5

1

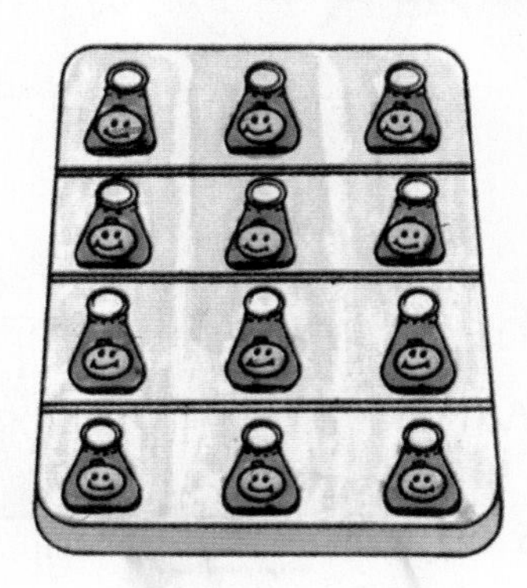

$\frac{1}{4}$ of 8 = 2 $\frac{1}{4}$ of 12 = 3 $\frac{1}{4}$ of 16 = 4

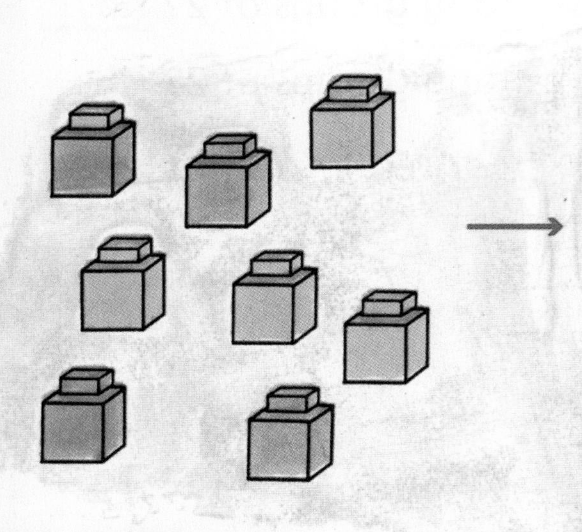

$\frac{1}{4}$ of 8 is 2

Use cubes.

2 $\frac{1}{4}$ of 20 = 5 $\frac{1}{4}$ of 24 = 6

3 Ron had 28 postcards.
He posted a quarter of them.

How many did he post? 7

4 Sue had 20 balloons.
She burst a quarter of them.

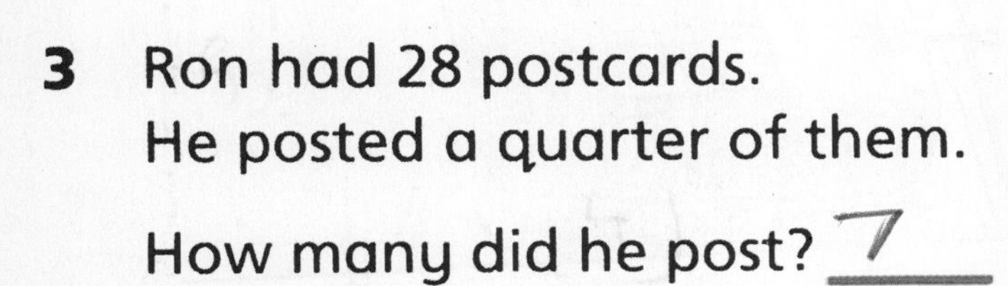

How many did she burst? 5

Beach fun

1 8 children go on the swings.
There are 2 to a swing.

How many groups of 2? 4

Use cubes or counters.

2 10 children go on the swings. How many groups of 2? 5

12 children go on the swings. How many groups of 2? 6

14 children go on the swings. How many groups of 2? 7

3 9 children go boating. How many groups of 3? 3

15 children go boating. How many groups of 3? 5

18 children go boating. How many groups of 3? 6

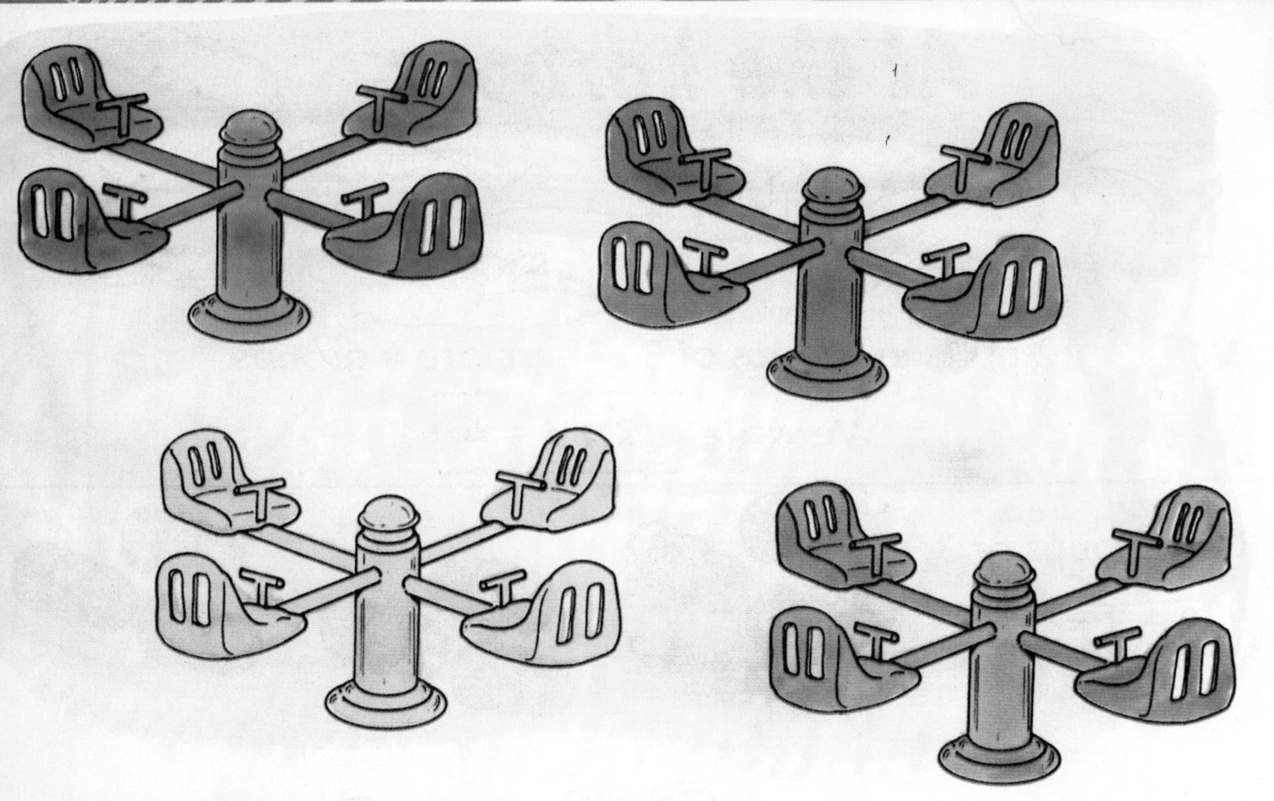

1 The children sit in groups of 4.

8 children. How many groups of 4? 2

16 children. How many groups of 4? 4

12 children. How many groups of 4? 3

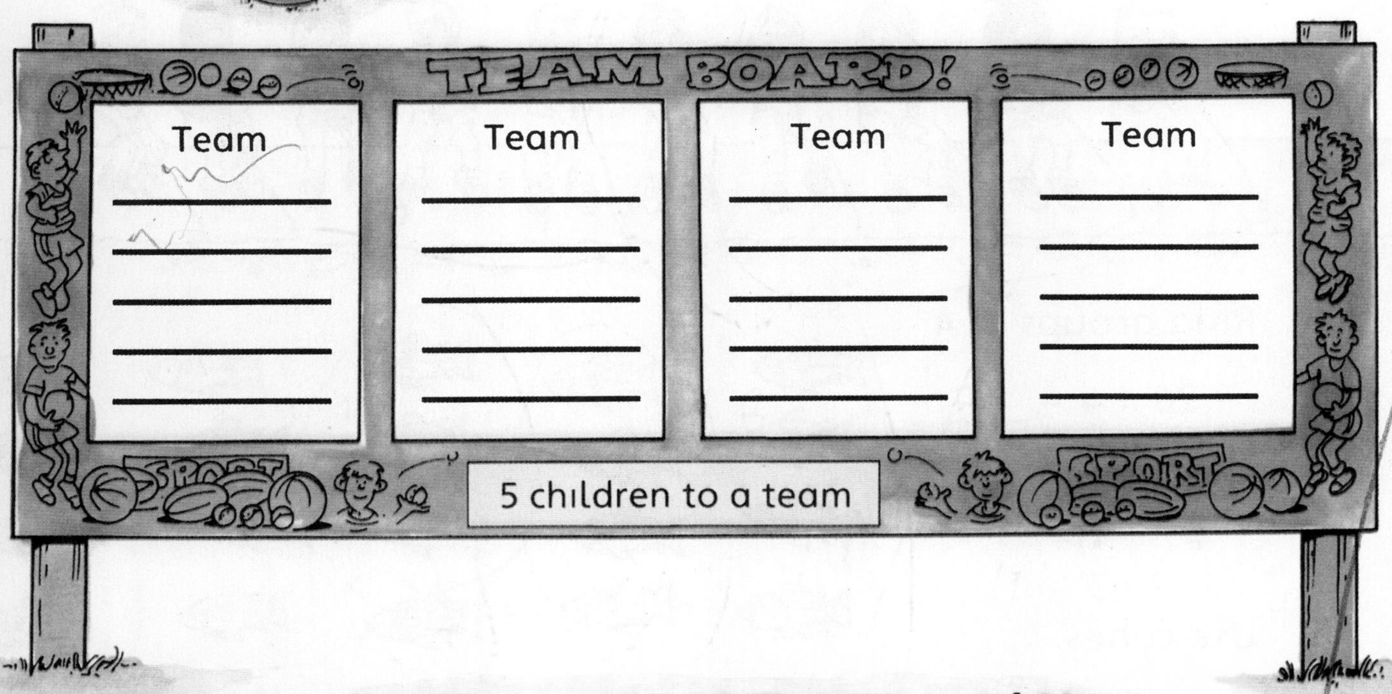

2 10 children are playing. How many groups of 5? 2

15 children are playing. How many groups of 5? 3

20 children are playing. How many groups of 5? 4

At the harbour

12 gulls in groups of 3. There are 4 groups.

We write **12 ÷ 3 = 4**

1 Ring groups of 3.

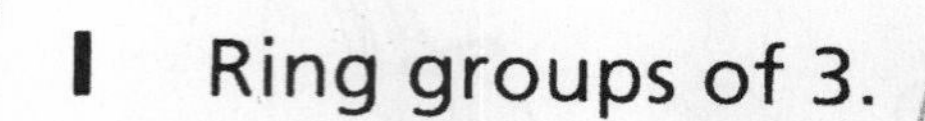

9 ÷ 3 = 3

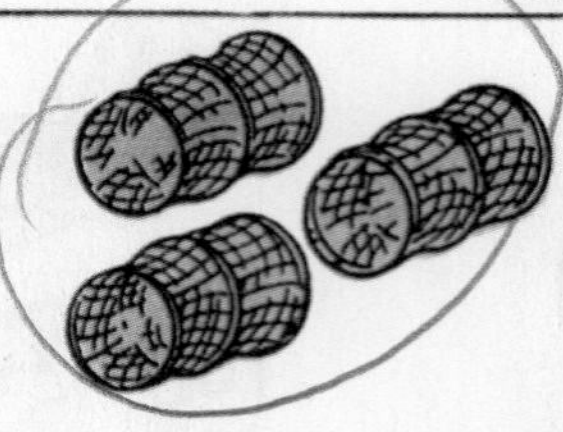

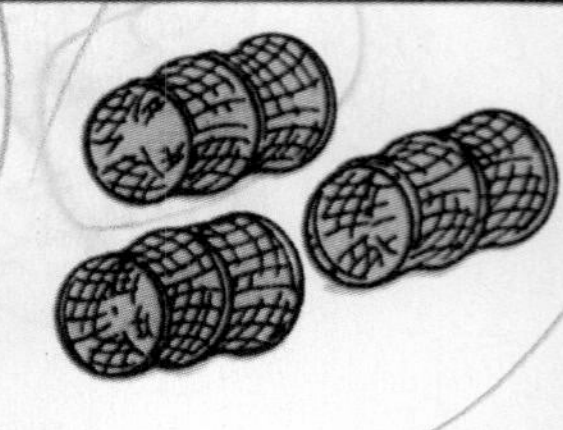

2 Ring groups of 2.

12 ÷ 2 = 6

3 Ring groups of 5. 10 ÷ 5 = 2

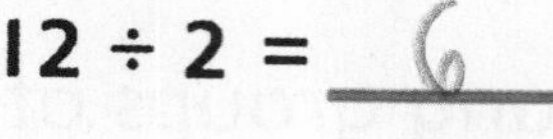

4 Ring groups of 4.

20 ÷ 4 = 5

5 Use cubes.

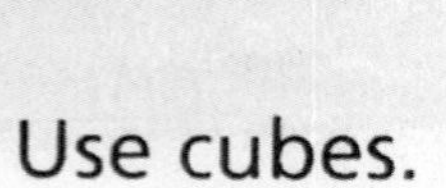

8 ÷ 2 = 4	18 ÷ 3 = 6	24 ÷ 3 = 8
20 ÷ 5 = 4	14 ÷ 2 = 7	21 ÷ 3 = 7
16 ÷ 4 = 4	15 ÷ 5 = 3	24 ÷ 3 = 8

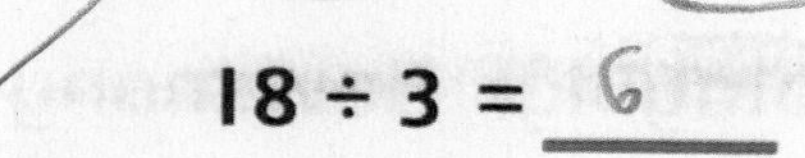
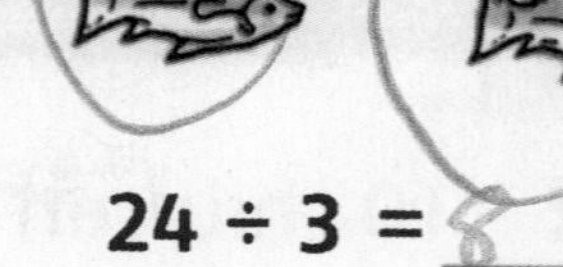

Boats

14 boats in groups of 3.

There are 4 groups and 2 left over.

14 ÷ 3 **is 4 remainder 2**

We write **14 ÷ 3 = 4 r 2**

1 How many boats? 9

How many groups of 4? 2

How many left over? 1

9 ÷ 4 = 2 r 1

Use cubes.

2 16 boats. Make groups of 3. **16 ÷ 3 =** 5 **r** 1

11 ÷ 3 = 3 **r** 4	**15 ÷ 2 =** 7 **r** 1
14 ÷ 4 = 3 **r** 2	**15 ÷ 4 =** 3 **r** 3
14 ÷ 5 = 2 **r** 4	**16 ÷ 5 =** 3 r 1
19 ÷ 4 = 4 r 3	**18 ÷ 4 =** 4 r 2
18 ÷ 2 = 9 r 0	**20 ÷ 3 =** 6 r 2

Extension

3 Write number stories for these.

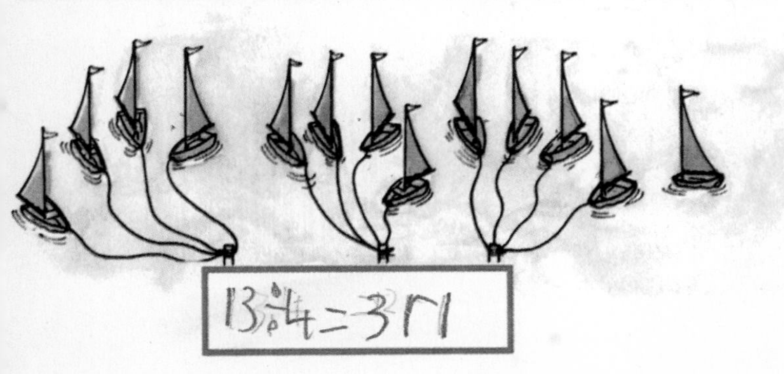

13 ÷ 4 = 3 r 1

10 ÷ 3 = 3 r 1

HEINEMANN MATHEMATICS

Workbook 2: Record of Work

Name ______________________ Class ______________

Workbook 2 / Textbook / Reinforcement Sheets / Check-ups

Topic										
Concept of multiplication	W1	W2	W3	W4	W5					
2 and 3 times tables	W6	W7	W8	R15	W9	W10	R16	T17	T18	Check-up 1
4 and 5 times tables	W11	W12	R17	W13	W14	R18	W15	W16		
Commutative aspect, 10 times table	W17	W18	W19	Check-up 2						
Money: the £1 coin	W20									
Using the 2, 3, 4, 5 and 10 times tables	W21	R19	W22	W23	W24	T19	T20	Check-up 3		
Other activities	T21									
Concept of division: sharing	W25	W26	W27	W28	R20	W29	R21	W30	T22	Check-up 4
Halves and quarters	W31	W32	W33	W34	R22	Check-up 5				
Concept of division: grouping	W35	W36	W37	R23	W38	R24	Check-up 6	Check-up 7		
Other activities	T23	T24	T25	T26						

Assessment Context 3	The Dream	
Assessment Context 4	Max	
Assessment Context 5	The Shopping Centre	

Heinemann is an imprint of Pearson Education Limited, a company incorporated in England and Wales, having its registered office at Edinburgh Gate, Harlow, Essex, CM20 2JE.
Registered company number: 872828
Pack of 8 ISBN 978 0 435 03780 2. Single copy ISBN 978 0 435 03099 5

First published 1992. Revised edition 12 21
Produced by Oxprint Ltd, Oxford. Illustrated by Oxford Illustrators.
Printed and bound in Malaysia, CTP-PJB

ISBN 978-0-435030-99-5